FLOWMETERS

FLOWMETERS

A BASIC GUIDE AND SOURCE-BOOK FOR USERS

Alan T. J. Hayward

First published 1979 by
THE MACMILLAN PRESS LTD
London and Basingstoke
Associated companies in Delhi Dublin
Hong Kong Johannesburg Lagos Melbourne
New York Singapore and Tokyo

Typeset by
Reproduction Drawings Ltd, Sutton, Surrey
Printed in Great Britain by
Unwin Brothers Limited, The Gresham Press
Old Woking, Surrey

British Library Cataloguing in Publication Data

Hayward, A T J
   Flowmeters.
   1. Flow meters
   I. Title
   $532'.053$ TC177

   ISBN 0-333-21920-1

To Peggy

Who has given me —

— thirty years of happy married life
— two fine children
— and her loyal support while I have struggled through the production of half a dozen books (although only another author's wife will be able to appreciate what that means!)

Contents

Preface

My main aim in this book has been to tell the man in the works office, who probably has an overflowing in-tray and a harassed look on his face, almost everything he really needs to know about fluid flowmeters. What I have tried to do is to state in simple language:

(1) just enough about every important kind of flowmeter to help him decide which is—and, perhaps more significantly, which is not—suitable for use in any combination of circumstances he is likely to come across;

(2) how to use flowmeters to their best advantage, thus saving both time and money, and what to do when their performance falls off;

(3) the best places to obtain further information on any particular aspect of flow metering.

With any luck this means that the book will tell him the answer to 90 per cent of his questions, and will advise him where to find an answer to nine out of the remaining ten. That leaves one question in a hundred which, in all probability, simply cannot be answered by anyone at present—otherwise there would be no justification for all those fellows beavering away in research laboratories.

The plan of the book is quite simple and can be seen at a glance from the detailed table of contents. This should enable the reader to find his way about in it easily. Although the book is intended for straightforward reading there is a detailed index at the end and a flowmeter selection table in Chapter 9, which should make things easy for the enquirer with no time to spare who wants to use the book as a work of reference.

To keep the book small it has been necessary to cut out nearly all the frills. Above all else a user wants to know exactly what a flowmeter will do, and to a limited extent he is interested to see how it does it. However, he is unlikely to enthuse about the finer points of theory and the long, contorted trail of engineering evolution which lies behind today's model.

So I have taken all the mathematical proofs for granted and resolutely refused to explore any fascinating but profitless blind-alleys. Likewise, the bibliography at the end of the book is not designed to show how much (or how little!) the author has read: it is there to point the way to the relatively few books, standard specifications and original papers of first-rate importance.

There has been no attempt to mention every individual flowmeter on the market, of which there are certainly hundreds and possibly thousands; that would have been rather pointless, and quite impossible in a short book. Instead, I have tried to describe every class of flowmeter which, in my opinion, it is well worth a mechanical or chemical engineer's while to know about—and that has still necessitated describing several dozen basic types. (Civil engineers may feel disappointed that there is no mention of weirs and flumes and other structures used to measure the flow of rivers and open channels. I am sorry about this omission, but there are two good reasons for it: opinions differ on whether these can properly be classed as flowmeters and I have used up my whole ration of space, anyway.)

However, I may well have failed to meet even this limited objective. New flowmeters are coming on the market almost every year and one or two valuable devices could easily have been overlooked. If so, it may be possible to rectify the omissions in a future edition or reprint. Should you have a pet flowmeter which to your great disappointment has not been mentioned, do please send me some information about it. Obviously I cannot promise to adopt every suggestion sent to me, but they will all be considered carefully.

Leamington Spa, 1979   *A.T.J.H*

Acknowledgements

When I began writing this book I had the good fortune to be working in the Flow Measurement Division of Britain's National Engineering Laboratory—an organisation which is justly proud of its reputation as the 'flow measurement centre for Europe'. I am grateful to the Director of NEL for allowing me to publish the book, and for permission to reproduce a number of illustrations from NEL publications.

On a more personal level, I am deeply indebted to a number of friends who read the first draft of those chapters where they felt most at home and suggested a great many improvements. In particular, I am grateful to Dr E A Spencer, the Head of Flow Measurement Division, NEL, who gave me much useful information as well as commenting upon the full text of the first draft. Mr R S Medlock, the former Technical Director of the George Kent Group, also gave most generously of his time to work through the complete text. Helpful comments were made on portions of the first draft by Professor R C Baker, Dr T J S Brain, Mr B C Ferguson, Mr R W F Gould, Mr P Harrison, Dr J J Hunter, Mr K I Jespersen, Dr F C Kinghorn, Mr L M Macdonald, Dr W C Pursley and Mr R W W Scott.

Finally, I must express my gratitude to two other friends and former colleagues: Mr A M Nicolson who edited the text and gave a great deal of useful advice on the preparation of the illustrations, and Mrs Bessie Pollock who traced all the line diagrams and graphs.

Notation

A	Cross-sectional area of pipe
B	Magnetic flux density
C	Coefficient of discharge of a flowmeter, $(=Q_T/Q_I)$ or other dimensionless calibration coefficient
c	Concentration of one substance in another
c_p	Specific heat capacity at constant pressure
D	Diameter of pipe
d	Diameter of a constriction—for example, the throat of a venturi tube
F	Meter factor $(= V_T/V_I)$
f	Frequency
g	Acceleration of gravity
H	Power supplied in the form of heat; or, height
H_n	Hodgson number
K	'K-factor' $(=n/V_T)$
K_n	Nominal K-factor
L	Length
M	Mass
m	Area ratio $(= A_2/A_1$ where A_2 and A_1 are throat and upstream cross-sections, respectively)
n	Meter pulse count
P	Pressure
δP	Pressure difference
Q	Flowrate
Q_I	Indicated flowrate
Q_M	Mass flowrate $(= dM/dt)$
Q_T	'True' flowrate (as measured by a calibration standard)
Q_V	Volumetric flowrate $(= dV/dt)$
q	One-pulse volume $(= 1/K)$
R	Radius
Re_D	Reynolds number (based on pipe diameter) $(= \rho \bar{v} D/\eta)$
Re_d	Reynolds number (based on meter throat diameter)

T	Temperature
t	Time
U	Voltage
V	Volume
V_I	Indicated volume
V_s	Specific volume ($= V/M$)
V_T	'True' volume (as measured by a calibration standard)
v	Velocity at a point
v_I	Indicated velocity
v_T	'True' velocity (as measured by a calibration standard)
$\bar{v}$	Mean velocity over a cross-section
Y	Flowmeter readout
β	Thermal expansion coefficient ($= \left\{1/V_s\right\}\left\{dV_s/dT\right\}$); or, diameter ratio ($= d/D$)
γ	Shear strain
$\dot{\gamma}$	Rate of shear strain
Δ	Meter correction ($= \left\{V_T - V_I\right\}/V_I$)
ϵ	Expansibility factor
η	Viscosity ($= \tau/\dot{\gamma}$)
κ	Compressibility ($= -\left\{1/V_s\right\}\left\{dV_s/dP\right\}$)
ν	Kinematic viscosity ($= \eta/\rho$)
ρ	Density
τ	Shear stress

1

Basic Principles of Fluid Flow

Ol' man river, dat ol' man river,
He must know sumpin', but don't say nothin',
He jus' keeps rollin',
He keeps on rollin' along.

Oscar Hammerstein II

1.1 Some Important Properties of Fluids

This book is about measuring the flow of fluids, and especially of fluids contained in pipes and ducts. To understand this subject it is useful to know something about the way fluids behave, and especially about the properties mentioned below.

1.1.1 Density and Specific Volume

The density of a fluid, ρ, is the ratio of its mass, M, to its volume, V. Its specific volume, V_s, is the reciprocal of its density. That is to say

$$\rho = \frac{1}{V_s} = \frac{M}{V} \tag{1.1}$$

The density of water is very roughly a thousand times that of air at atmospheric pressure.

1.1.2 Thermal Expansion Coefficient

The thermal expansion coefficient of a fluid, β, otherwise known as its coefficient of volumetric expansion, or its coefficient of cubical expansion, is the fractional increase in specific volume (or the fractional decrease in density) caused by a temperature increase of $1°$. The mathematical definition is

$$\beta = \frac{1}{V_s} \frac{dV_s}{dT} = -\frac{1}{\rho} \frac{d\rho}{dT} \tag{1.2}$$

1

The thermal expansion coefficient of cold water is very small, and is usually disregarded except when very high accuracy is required, but it increases rapidly with increasing temperature. The thermal expansion coefficients of oils and liquid fuels, however, are practically independent of temperature (except when they are very hot); they are very much greater than that of cold water and cannot be neglected in accurate work. Thermal expansion in gases is greater still, and must always be taken into account.

Some typical values of thermal expansion coefficient are as follows.

Water at 20°C	0.0002 per °C
Hydrocarbons, in the region of	0.001 per °C
Air at 20°C	0.0034 per °C

1.1.3 Compressibility

The compressibility of a fluid, κ, is the fractional *decrease* in specific volume (or the fractional *increase* in density) caused by unit increase of pressure. In the language of mathematics

$$\kappa = -\frac{1}{V_s}\frac{dV_s}{dP} = \frac{1}{\rho}\frac{d\rho}{dP} \tag{1.3}$$

The old saw that 'liquids are incompressible' is a myth—they are slightly compressible. The compressibility of water, for example, is approximately 0.000 05 per bar, which is about one twenty-thousandth of that of air at atmospheric pressure, and for most purposes can be ignored. The compressibility of liquid petroleum products varies with their composition, viscous oils being only a little more compressible than water and light fuels being more than twice as compressible as water. In the large-scale commercial metering of oils and fuels compressibility is generally taken into account when pressures above about 2 bar are encountered.

Gases are very highly compressible at low pressures, but much less so at high pressures: the compressibility of an ideal gas is inversely proportional to its absolute pressure. The extent to which the behaviour of real gases differs from the ideal is expressed as a 'gas law deviation coefficient' or a 'supercompressibility factor', values of which are listed for various gases in several of the books and standards on differential pressure metering, which are referenced in Chapter 3.

1.1.4 Viscosity

The viscosity, η, of a fluid is a measure of its resistance to shearing at a constant rate. In terms of *Figure 1.1* the mathematicians' definition is

$$\eta = \frac{\tau}{\dot{\gamma}} \tag{1.4}$$

where τ is the shear stress, and $\dot{\gamma}$ is the rate of shear strain.

(In common parlance, the viscosity of a liquid is its 'thickness'.)

The SI unit of viscosity is the Pascal second (Pa s), but it is usual to express viscosities in centipoise (cP), one cP being 10^{-3} Pa s. Viscosity is often referred to as 'absolute viscosity' or 'dynamic viscosity', to distinguish it from *kinematic viscosity*, ν; this is an entirely different property, being the ratio of viscosity to density, η/ρ. The SI unit of kinematic viscosity is m^2 s^{-1}, and the common unit the centistokes (cSt), one cSt being 10^{-6} m^2 s^{-1}.

To get a feeling of what viscosity values mean, it is useful to memorise the following table. The values quoted are at normal ambient temperatures; viscosity falls rapidly with increasing temperature.

Substance	Approximate viscosity (cP)
Air	0.02
Water	1
Engine oil	100
Gear oil	1000
Honey	100000

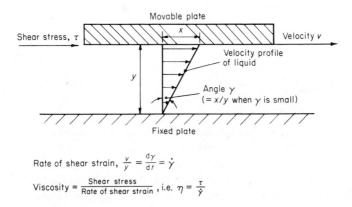

Rate of shear strain, $\dfrac{v}{y} = \dfrac{d\gamma}{dt} = \dot{\gamma}$

Viscosity $= \dfrac{\text{Shear stress}}{\text{Rate of shear strain}}$, i.e. $\eta = \dfrac{\tau}{\dot{\gamma}}$

Figure 1.1 *Basis of definition of viscosity*

Viscosity can be measured conveniently in a concentric-cylinder viscometer *(Figure 1.2)*, or, more accurately, in a U-tube viscometer *(Figure 1.3)*.

Some liquids, including molten polymers and suspensions of solids in liquids, have a viscosity that varies with the rate of shear strain, $\dot{\gamma}$. They are termed 'non-Newtonian' and their behaviour is very complex; they are outside the scope of this book.

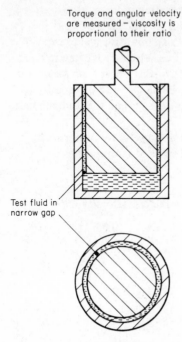

Torque and angular velocity
are measured − viscosity is
proportional to their ratio

Test fluid in
narrow gap

Figure 1.2 *Principle of the
concentric-cylinder viscometer*

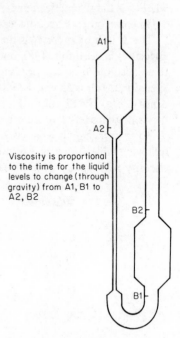

A1

A2

Viscosity is proportional
to the time for the liquid
levels to change (through
gravity) from A1, B1 to
A2, B2

B2

B1

Figure 1.3 *Principle of the
U-tube viscometer*

1.1.5 Air Solubility of Liquids

Air is soluble in liquids, and its solubility is directly proportional to the absolute pressure. The solubility of air in cold water is about 2% by volume (measured at standard temperature and pressure) when the absolute pressure is 1 bar, 4% when it is 2 bar, 1% when it is 0.5 bar, and so on. The solubility decreases markedly as the temperature of the water increases. It is very much more soluble in hydrocarbons: typical values at 1 bar are 8% in lubricating oil, 12% in kerosene and 16% in gasoline. Moreover, these values are not decreased much with increasing temperature, until quite high temperatures are reached.

Dissolved air is likely to be released from solution in oils and fuels if the pressure is allowed to fall momentarily much below atmospheric, and the resulting air bubbles in the liquid can cause metering errors (see section 10.3). Decreased pressures and increased temperatures can also produce air bubbles in water, but the quantities of air released from solution in water are normally very much less than in oils and fuels.

1.1.6 Humidity in Gases

Gases may be either dry or humid (damp). This is because a gas at a given temperature is capable of holding up to a certain maximum amount of water vapour; this maximum amount increases as the temperature increases. When a gas is holding the maximum amount of water vapour it is said to be 'saturated' with water vapour. If it is unsaturated, its degree of saturation may be expressed as a 'relative humidity'; this is defined as the ratio of the actual partial pressure of the water vapour to the value of the partial pressure that would exist under saturated conditions at the same temperature. ('Partial pressure' means the pressure the water vapour would exert if the same quantity of it were to fill the same volume without any air being present.)

The humidity of a gas affects its density. For example, in the case of air at 1 bar and 20°C, the density when dry is about 1.5% greater than the density when saturated with water vapour.

Sudden changes in humidity may cause errors in gas flow measurement. In particular, errors can easily occur if unsaturated gas is passed through a 'wet gas meter' (see section 5.2.5), or if a sudden expansion cools a gas sufficiently to cause precipitation of some of its water vapour (see section 10.6).

1.2 Some Important Principles of Pipe Flow

More often than not flow measurement in industry is concerned with measuring the flow of fluids in pipes. It is therefore essential to understand the basic principles of pipe flow.

1.2.1 Reynolds Number

The behaviour of fluids flowing through pipes is governed by a quantity known as Reynolds number (Re_D). This is defined as

$$Re_D = \frac{\rho \bar{v} D}{\eta} \tag{1.5}$$

where $\bar{v}$ is the mean velocity, and D is the pipe diameter.

Engineers often seem to be rather scared of this quantity, as if it were too mysterious to comprehend. There is no need for this attitude. Reynolds number has a simple meaning.

Consider the numerator in equation 1.5, $\rho \bar{v} D$. ρ is mass per unit volume. Therefore $\rho \bar{v}$ is momentum per unit volume, and $\rho \bar{v} D$ is moment of momentum per unit volume. The numerator is thus a measure of the flowing fluid's ability to generate dynamic forces, whilst the denominator, η, is a measure of its ability to generate viscous forces. This means that Reynolds number indicates which kind of forces will predominate in the flowing fluid. When $\rho\bar{v}D$ is relatively large Re_D will be large and dynamic forces will prevail, but when η is relatively large Re_D will be smaller and viscous forces will prevail.

Incidentally, Re_D is called Reynolds *number* because the dimensions of $\rho\bar{v}D$ are the same as those of η, and Re_D is therefore a dimensionless ratio.

1.2.2 *Laminar and Turbulent Flow*

A fluid can flow along a pipe in either of two very different ways.

Laminar flow—or, as it is sometimes called, 'streamline flow', or 'viscous flow'—occurs at Reynolds numbers below about 2000. This can be likened to the flow of traffic on a busy motorway, with the traffic in the various lanes travelling on parallel paths at different speeds; the slow lane is next to the pipe wall and the fast lane in the centre of the pipe. When studying laminar flow in pipes engineers usually assume that the 'traffic' never changes lanes. In fact, gradual lane-changing does occur. It is called 'secondary flow' and is a very complex subject, which no doubt is why it is generally ignored in practical situations.

Turbulent flow occurs at Reynolds numbers above about 2000 (and sometimes at much lower Reynolds numbers, too). This can be likened to the flight of a flock of starlings. The flock as a whole may be travelling in a straight line at a constant speed, but if you watch the flight of any individual bird he will appear to be zig-zagging and gyrating wildly within the flock.

In industry, pipe Reynolds numbers are usually well above 2000 and laminar flow is rarely encountered, unless very viscous liquids are being piped. Throughout this book it can be assumed that turbulent flow is always being considered, unless laminar flow is specifically mentioned.

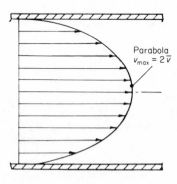

Figure 1.4 *Velocity profile in laminar flow*

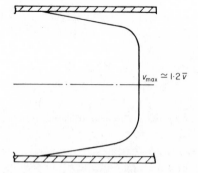

Figure 1.5 *A practically fully developed velocity profile in turbulent flow (from measurements at NEL)*

1.2.3 Velocity Profile

A graph showing how the velocity varies across a diameter of a pipe is called a velocity profile. Examples of three important types of velocity profile are given in *Figures 1.4–1.6.*

In laminar flow the velocity profile is a parabola, and the velocity in the centre of the pipe is twice the mean velocity *(Figure 1.4).*

With turbulent flow, the velocity profile at the downstream end of a very long length of straight pipe is very much flatter *(Figure 1.5),* and the velocity at the centre is about 1.2 times the mean velocity. Under these conditions the profile is said to be 'fully developed', or 'normal'. However, the profile can be greatly distorted by the presence of a bend in the pipe, or by a flowmeter or a valve, etc. *Figure 1.6* shows two typical asymmetrical profiles, derived from measurements with a laser velocimeter 5 and 20 diameters downstream of the same bend in a 75-mm pipe.

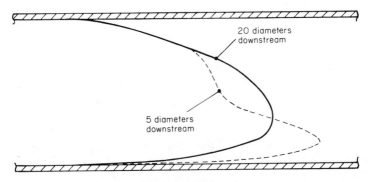

Figure 1.6 *Velocity profiles 5 and 20 diameters downstream of a bend in a pipe (from measurements at NEL)*

1.2.4 Rotation and Swirl

Bends, flowmeters, valves, etc., also produce what is known as rotation in the flow. The fluid on the outside of the bend has to travel farther than the fluid on the inside, and this distorts the pattern of flow in a highly complex fashion. One consequence of this is that a rotary motion, A, is superimposed on the forward velocity, B, in the downstream straight pipe. An oversimplified representation of this effect is shown in *Figure 1.7.*

The most severe kind of rotation is the three-dimensional rotational flow, or 'swirl', created by two adjacent disturbances or bends in different planes. This causes the flow to rotate in a corkscrew fashion, and the effect can persist for very long distances. At high Reynolds numbers it decays at the rate of about 4% per diameter, and at low Reynolds numbers at only about 2% per diameter[1] –

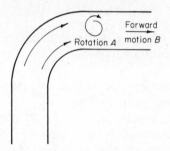

Figure 1.7 *A simplified representation of the rotation imparted by a pipe bend*

that is to say, in a pipe of, say, 100 mm diameter, the severity of the swirl present diminishes by only 4% (or 2%) for each 100 mm it travels along the pipe.

Severe swirl can, if necessary, be suppressed by the installation of a flow straightener (*see* section 10.2).

1.2.5 Continuity and Bernoulli's Equation

What goes in at one end of a pipe must come out at the other. This simple fact is the basis of the principle of continuity, which holds that the mass flowrate is the same at all cross-sections of one continuous pipe without branches. If the fluid is practically incompressible, the volumetric flowrate remains practically constant also.

This principle is of great importance when studying flowmeter behaviour. It means that when the cross-section decreases the mean velocity must increase and *vice versa*.

The total energy possessed by a flowing fluid is the same at every cross-section along the pipe. Bernoulli's equation expresses this fact in mathematical terms. A full expression for this equation is complicated, but if it is assumed that the pipe is horizontal and the fluid incompressible, and if such factors as the effect of fluid friction in turning some mechanical energy into heat, and the variation of velocity across the cross-section are ignored, Bernoulli's equation reduces to

$$P + \tfrac{1}{2}\rho\bar{v}^2 \; = \; \text{constant at all cross-sections} \qquad (1.6)$$

This simple equation is used to derive theoretical expressions for the behaviour of many types of flowmeter.

1.2.6 Velocity Head

The expression $\bar{v}^2/2g$, where g is the acceleration of gravity, provides a convenient way of indicating the amount of kinetic energy possessed by the fluid flowing in a pipe. It has the dimensions of length, and is equal to the height (head) to which the fluid would rise if it were projected vertically upwards at a velocity $\bar{v}$ in an ideal world where there was no such thing as friction.

An important use of this concept is to express the tendency of pipe fittings to dissipate energy. For example, if a certain flowmeter is said to cause a 'loss of 3 velocity heads', this means that the head loss across that meter will always be approximately $3\bar{v}^2/2g$, regardless of the nature of the fluid or its velocity.

1.2.7 Cavitation

It follows from equation 1.6 that when the mean velocity increases (as it must do when the cross-sectional area of flow is reduced) the pressure will decrease. In a flowing liquid, if the pressure drop is large enough, a phenomenon known as cavitation can occur. This can take two different forms.

In water, volatile hydrocarbons and liquefied gases cavitation generally occurs only when the pressure at some point approaches the vapour pressure of the liquid. Then bubbles or pockets of vapour appear, only to collapse as soon as they enter a region of higher pressure. If this occurs inside a flowmeter it will give wrong readings. When this sort of cavitation occurs in a severe form it often betrays its presence by a crackling noise.

In viscous oils and non-volatile liquid fuels cavitation generally takes a different form. It begins at pressures somewhat below atmospheric, but well above the vapour pressure, and consists of the release from solution of bubbles of air or gas. These bubbles take quite a long time to dissolve again, and can therefore affect the readings of flowmeters installed well downstream of the point of cavitation.

Both types of cavitation must be avoided if accurate flow metering is required (*see* section 10.3 for practical advice on this).

1.2.8 Double-block-and-bleed Valve Systems

Flowmeters are frequently installed in a complex network of piping containing a number of shut-off valves. If one of these valves leaks, it may enable part of the flow reaching a flowmeter to be bypassed around the meter, instead of passing through it. In such circumstances the operator needs some way of confirming that the key valves are sealing perfectly.

This is provided by what is known as the double-block-and-bleed system, shown in *Figure 1.8*. Two valves are installed in the main pipeline in place of

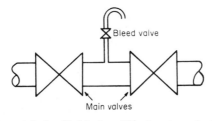

Figure 1.8 *Double-block-and-bleed system of valves*

the usual one, and a valved bleed tapping is connected to the space between the valves. If no fluid issues from the bleed when the system is pressurised and both the main valves are shut and the bleed valve is open, it follows that the main valves are leak-tight.

The same result may be achieved more compactly with a single valve possessing two sets of seals and a valved bleed tapping leading to the centre of the valve; this is known as a double-block-and-bleed valve.

Reference

1   Baker, D. W. and Sayre, C. L., 'Decay of swirling turbulent flow of incompressible fluids in long pipes'. In R. B. Dowdell (Ed.), *Flow, its Measurement and Control in Science and Industry, Vol. 1, Part 1,* Instrument Society of America, Pittsburgh, 301–312 (1974)

2

Basic Principles of Flow Measurement

The method employed I would gladly explain,
While I have it so clear in my head,
If I had but the time and you had but the brain—
But much yet remains to be said.

Lewis Carroll

2.1 What do You Want to Measure?

The term 'flow measurement' can refer to any of six different types of measurement. These are briefly described below.

2.1.1. Point Velocity Measurement

Instruments are available (*see* Chapter 7) with which the velocity, v, of a fluid at a point can be measured. These are often (though not invariably) called 'anemometers' if intended for use in free-flowing air, 'current meters' if intended for use in the sea or a river, and 'insertion meters' if intended for use inside a pipe or duct.

2.1.2 Mean Pipe Velocity Measurement

Mean pipe velocity, $\bar{v}$, is related to volumetric flowrate, Q_V (*see* section 2.1.3), and pipe cross-sectional area, A, by the relationship

$$Q_V = \bar{v}A \tag{2.1}$$

$\bar{v}$ can be determined in three ways: by measuring Q_V and A and then employing equation 2.1; by measuring v at numerous points on one cross-section and then taking an appropriately weighted mean (*see* section 7.9); or, less accurately, by measuring the velocity at a point three-quarters of the way from the pipe centre to the wall, since it is known that in fully developed profiles the velocity at that point is approximately equal to the mean velocity.

2.1.3 Volumetric Flowrate Measurement

Volumetric flowrate, Q_V, is defined as the rate of change of volume, V, with time, t. Thus

$$Q_V = \frac{dV}{dt} \tag{2.2}$$

If the flowrate is constant, this reduces to

$$Q_V = \frac{V}{t} \tag{2.3}$$

Many flowmeters are designed to indicate directly the value of Q_V; such meters are sometimes referred to as 'flowrate meters'.

2.1.4 Total Volume Measurement

Some meters are designed to indicate directly the total volume, V, passed through the meter; they are sometimes called 'volume meters', or 'bulk meters', to distinguish them from flowrate meters.

It follows from equations 2.2 and 2.3 that V can be derived from a flowrate meter by integrating its output over a period, and that one can derive Q_V from a volume meter by differentiating its output with respect to time. These operations usually result in some loss of accuracy, however.

2.1.5 Mass Flowrate Measurement

Mass flowrate, Q_M, is the rate of change of mass with time. That is

$$Q_M = \frac{dM}{dt} \tag{2.4}$$

At constant mass flowrate

$$Q_M = \frac{M}{t} \tag{2.5}$$

Some flowmeters are designed to indicate mass flowrate directly. They are called 'mass flowmeters', or 'true mass flowmeters' (see section 8.1).

Q_M is frequently determined by making simultaneous measurements of Q_V and ρ, and then employing the relationship

$$Q_M = \rho Q_V \tag{2.6}$$

2.1.6 Total Mass Measurement

There is as yet no flowmeter in widespread use which measures directly the total mass of fluid passing during a period. To determine M it is customary either to measure Q_M and integrate the measurements over a period using equation 2.4 or 2.5, or to measure V and ρ and then employ equation 1.1.

2.2 Characteristic Curves

A characteristic curve is a graph showing how the performance of a flowmeter varies with flowrate, or with velocity or Reynolds number in cases where one of these is more appropriate.

Such a curve is generally derived from a calibration, that is to say from a series of tests over a range of flowrates or velocities in which the reading of the flowmeter is compared with a measured value of flowrate (or of volume, or of mass, or of velocity, if this is what the flowmeter concerned is designed to indicate) derived from a measuring device of high accuracy (*see* Chapter 11).

2.2.1 Linear and Non-Linear Flowmeters

In principle, the results of a calibration may be plotted as a graph of flowmeter readout, Y, against flowrate, Q. If the graph forms a more-or-less straight line through the origin, as in *Figure 2.1*, the flowmeter is described as 'linear'. Most non-linear flowmeters have a characteristic of the form shown in *Figure 2.2*, where Q is proportional to $Y^{\frac{1}{2}}$. Venturimeters, orifice plates and pitot tubes, where Y is a measured value of pressure difference, come into this category.

2.2.2 Use of a Flowmeter Performance Index

In practice, graphs of the form shown in *Figures 2.1* and *2.2* are rarely used, because they are not capable of showing sufficient detail. What is needed is a

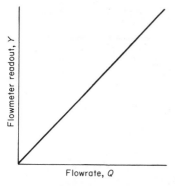

Figure 2.1 *Linear flowmeter characteristic curve*

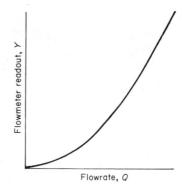

Figure 2.2 *Non-linear flowmeter characteristic curve*

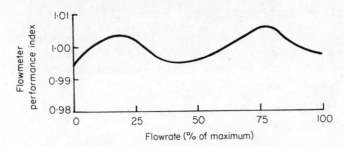

Figure 2.3 *Use of a performance index enables flowmeter calibration characteristics to be exhibited more clearly*

graph that clearly displays any small deviations from ideal behaviour by the flowmeter.

It is therefore usual to plot some kind of flowmeter performance index against flowrate or against some comparable quantity such as Reynolds number, as illustrated in *Figure 2.3*. The closer the resulting graph is to a horizontal straight line, the closer is the performance of the flowmeter to the ideal.

Numerous types of index are possible, but only four are in common use. They are briefly described below.

2.2.3 *Coefficient of Discharge*

Coefficient of discharge, C, is defined for flowrate meters by the equation

$$C = \frac{Q_T}{Q_I} \tag{2.7}$$

and for velocity meters by the equation

$$C = \frac{v_T}{v_I} \tag{2.8}$$

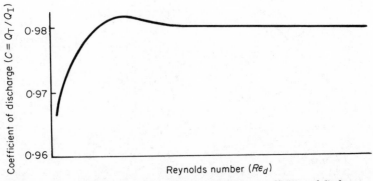

Figure 2.4 *Example of characteristic curve based on coefficient of discharge*

where Q_T and v_T denote what is commonly called 'true' flowrate and 'true' velocity, by which is meant these quantities as measured by the high-accuracy device used in the calibration; and Q_I and v_I denote the flowrate or velocity indicated by the meter, or calculated from its readings.

Coefficient of discharge is used extensively in connection with differential pressure meters (see Chapter 3) and is generally plotted against Re_d, the Reynolds number at the throat of the meter, as in *Figure 2.4*.

2.2.4 Meter Correction

Meter correction, Δ, is a term used in connection with volume meters of the type that read directly in volume units, especially displacement meters. It is defined as

$$\Delta = \frac{V_T - V_I}{V_I} \tag{2.9}$$

where V_T and V_I denote 'true' and indicated volume, respectively. It may be expressed either as a fraction or as a percentage.

The negative of this, $-\Delta$, is often called 'meter error'—a phrase which can be misunderstood and is therefore best avoided.

2.2.5 Meter Factor

Meter factor, F, is a term mainly used in connection with meters used for measuring total volume, and especially with turbine meters and positive displacement meters. Unfortunately, different writers have defined it in several different ways and this has caused great confusion in the past, but it is now generally agreed that the correct definition is

$$F = \frac{V_T}{V_I} \tag{2.10}$$

It follows from equations 2.9 and 2.10 that

$$F = 1 + \Delta \tag{2.11}$$

2.2.6 K-Factor

K-factor is a term used to describe the performance of meters such as turbine meters whose output is in the form of a series of electrical pulses, and where the total pulse count, n, is nominally proportional to the volume passed, and the pulse frequency, dn/dt, is nominally proportional to the flowrate. It is defined as

$$K = \frac{n}{V_T} \tag{2.12}$$

Characteristic curves for turbine meters customarily take the form of a graph of K-factor against flowrate, as in *Figure 2.5*.

The reciprocal of K-factor is a quantity of great practical importance, since, every time such a meter is used, $1/K$ must be multiplied by the meter pulse count, n, to derive the volume passed by the meter. It is therefore regrettable that $1/K$ has not previously been given a name; in this book it will be termed the 'one-pulse volume', q.

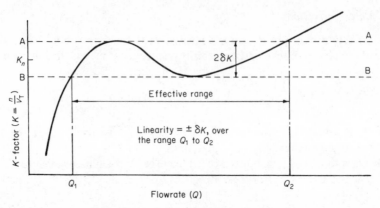

Figure 2.5 *Example of characteristic curve based on K-factor (also illustrating meaning of the terms 'effective range' and 'linearity')*

2.3 Properties of Measuring Instruments

A few terms are discussed below which relate to measuring instruments in general. They are of especial importance when considering the properties of flowmeters.

2.3.1 Discrimination

By international agreement[1], the word 'discrimination' is used to describe how finely an instrument can measure. For example, the discrimination of a digital electronic timer reading in milliseconds is a hundred times as great as that of a stopwatch graduated in tenths of a second. Discrimination is often wrongly referred to as 'sensitivity', which by international agreement means something very different, and as 'resolution', which has no internationally agreed meaning; it is worth making a conscious effort to avoid using these incorrect terms.

Do not confuse discrimination with accuracy. Discrimination decides how many decimal places you can read to; it tells you nothing about how many of those decimal places you can rely upon.

Figure 2.6 *Do not confuse repeatability with accuracy!* (a) Poor repeatability means poor accuracy, (b) good accuracy means good repeatability and (c) good repeatability does *not* necessarily mean good accuracy. (Cartoons courtesy NEL)

2.3.2 Repeatability

The repeatability of an instrument is an indication of its ability to give the same
result when it is used to measure the same quantity several times in succession.
A numerical value of repeatability can be obtained experimentally by installing
two nominally identical flowmeters in series and comparing their readings many
times in succession[2].

Repeatability is often confused with accuracy, which, as *Figure 2.6* shows,
is not the same thing at all. If an instrument has poor repeatability it is bound to
have poor accuracy also; but if it has good repeatability that does not necessarily
mean it will have good accuracy (although it might have), since it could be
giving the same wrong answer time after time.

2.3.3 Accuracy

If one thinks of repeatability as the measure of an instrument's ability to stick to
the same story, accuracy is a measure of its ability to tell the truth. In general,
good repeatability depends upon good design and careful manufacture, whereas
good accuracy depends upon those two things plus a third: accurate calibration
against a standard (*see* Chapter 11). Where it is essential for high accuracy to be
maintained over a period, recalibration at intervals may be needed.

Much confusion is caused by the existence of two very different methods of
expressing accuracy. Some manufacturers quote it as a percentage of *full-scale*
reading, others as a percentage of *actual* reading. The difference becomes highly
significant when an instrument is working near the bottom of its range: for
example, at one-fifth of the scale maximum an accuracy of 1% of full scale is
equal to an accuracy of 5% of reading. In this book, unless otherwise stated,
quoted accuracies are always expressed as a percentage of actual reading.

Remember that good repeatability costs a lot, and good accuracy costs even
more. It is extravagant to install a highly repeatable instrument where a cheap
one would do; and equally wasteful to install a highly *accurate,* well calibrated
instrument if all you need is good *repeatability*—which may well be the case if
you are only using it for control purposes. High accuracy is, however, needed if
you are buying, selling or paying duty against meter readings. The best way to
ensure high accuracy is by using a meter of high repeatability in conjunction
with a 'dedicated' (that is, permanently built in) calibration device (*see*
section 11.1.5).

How to estimate the accuracy of a flowrate measurement is the subject of a
draft international standard[3].

The word 'uncertainty' is often used as a synonym for accuracy, although,
strictly speaking, uncertainty is the property of a measurement rather than the
instrument used to make the measurement.

2.3.4 Effective Range and Rangeability

The effective range of an instrument is defined[4] as the range over which it meets some specified accuracy requirements. This definition is illustrated in *Figure 2.5,* where the horizontal lines AA and BB represent the permitted limits of accuracy, and the effective range is therefore from Q_1 to Q_2. The ratio Q_2/Q_1 is often called the 'rangeability' of an instrument, or, in the case of a flowmeter, its 'turndown ratio', or simply, 'turndown'.

2.3.5 Linearity

The linearity of an instrument is a measure of the extent to which its calibration curve over its effective range departs from the best fitting straight line. In *Figure 2.5,* where the accuracy limits are drawn $2\delta K$ apart, the linearity is $\pm\delta K$. It is usually expressed as a percentage of the nominal calibration factor, K_n, that is, in the case illustrated, as $100\ \delta K/K_n$ per cent.

References

1 *Vocabulary of Legal Metrology*, International Organisation of Legal Metrology, Paris (1969). English edition, British Standards Institution, London (1969)
2 Hayward, A. T. J., *Repeatability and Accuracy,* Mechanical Engineering Publications Ltd., London (1977)
3 *ISO Draft International Standard 5168 (1976).* Estimation of the uncertainty of a measurement of flowrate
4 *British Standard 2643 (1955).* Glossary of terms relating to the performance of measuring instruments

3

Differential Pressure Meters

I just stand up and spout.

A. E. Housman

3.1 Introduction

For many years, differential pressure meters were the only devices available for measuring volumetric flowrate in a pipe with reasonable accuracy at a reasonable cost. Nowadays there are many alternatives, but even so, the differential pressure meter family still holds the largest slice of the market.

3.1.1 Advantages

The popularity of differential pressure meters is probably due to the following collection of advantages.

(a) Simplicity of construction: there are no moving parts to go wrong inside the pipe, and any electrical readout equipment is wholly on the outside of the pipe where it can be easily serviced.

(b) Versatility: they can be used with almost any fluid, from superheated steam to sulphuric acid.

(c) Economy: by choosing the right kind of differential pressure meter, one can have either a low initial cost, or a low head loss and hence low pumping costs—but not both together.

(d) Experience: there is an abundance of published information, and of advice enshrined in codes of practice, relating to differential pressure meters used in very many different ways.

3.1.2 Disadvantages

(a) The accuracy is not quite as high as that of some of the more modern types of meter—especially if, as is commonly the case, the differential pressure meter is sold without calibration for the sake of cheapness. (The actual accuracies obtainable depend on circumstances, but as a very rough guide figures of ±1% if calibrated and ±2 or 3% if uncalibrated may be borne in mind.)

(b) The output signal, differential pressure, is not linear with flowrate, but is proportional to Q_V^2. This not only necessitates the extraction of a square root every time a reading is taken (which is no great problem with modern data processors), but, more seriously, it means that the rangeability of this type of flowmeter is generally much lower than that of flowmeters with a linear output.

3.1.3 Basic Principles

The meter depends upon the fact that when a fluid flows through a contraction it must accelerate; this causes its kinetic energy to increase, and consequently its pressure must fall by a corresponding amount, in accordance with the principle of the conservation of energy. In *Figure 3.1*, fluid at a mean velocity, $\bar{v}_1$, and density, ρ_1, passes a cross-section of area, A_1; then it passes the smaller cross-section, A_2, at $\bar{v}_2$ and ρ_2.

By applying both Bernoulli's equation and the principle of continuity (*see* section 1.2.5) between these two cross-sections, it can be shown that for an ideal and incompressible fluid

$$Q_V = \frac{A_2}{(1 - m^2)^{\frac{1}{2}}} \left(\frac{2\delta P}{\rho_1} \right)^{\frac{1}{2}} \tag{3.1}$$

where m is the 'area ratio', A_2/A_1, and δP is the measured 'differential pressure' $(P_1 - P_2)$ between the two cross-sections.

Unfortunately, real fluids are not ideal, and an empirical coefficient, C, known as the 'coefficient of discharge', must be introduced to allow for this. Also, if the

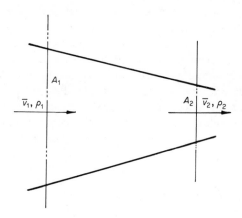

Figure 3.1 *Flow through a contraction in a pipe*

fluid is a gas, a second empirical coefficient, the 'expansibility factor', ϵ, must be introduced. This depends upon the physical properties of the gas being metered, as well as the geometry of the flowmeter. The equation for practical use then becomes

$$Q_V = \frac{C\epsilon A_2}{(1 - m^2)^{1/2}} \left(\frac{2\delta P}{\rho_1} \right)^{1/2} \tag{3.2}$$

If the highest possible accuracy is required, the coefficient, C, must be obtained by calibrating the meter over a range of flowrates. Where an accuracy around ±2% is acceptable, values of C for each type of meter can be obtained from national[1] and international[2] standard specifications; tabulated values of ϵ are obtainable from them, too. These standards also specify the main geometrical requirements for each type of meter and provide standard methods for calculating the uncertainty (accuracy) likely to be obtained under various conditions of use.

A complete differential pressure meter consists of two parts: the piece that fits into the pipe and generates the differential pressure is known as the 'primary' whilst the associated device for measuring the differential pressure is called the 'secondary'. This chapter is concerned only with the various types of primary device, while secondary devices are dealt with in Chapter 12.

3.1.4 Selecting a Differential Pressure Meter

The main kinds of differential pressure meter in common use are described below. It is usually not difficult to decide which broad type is best for a particular job. The lengthy, expensive venturimeter has a low head loss and its high initial cost is therefore justified in situations where large quantities of liquid are being pumped more or less continuously—for example, in main water supply pipelines. Where head loss is not very important, as is often the case in process plants and in gas lines, the cheapness of the orifice plate is the decisive factor. If a compromise is required, the nozzle is of intermediate size and cost, although it creates practically the same head loss as an orifice plate.

The choice of which area ratio to adopt is more difficult. Too high an area ratio will provide insufficient differential pressure for accurate measurement, while an excessively low ratio will create an unnecessarily high head loss. Deciding on the optimum area ratio for a particular duty requires a fairly detailed knowledge of the subject, and generally involves some complicated calculations. Most users will find it helpful to seek advice on this from manufacturers or specialist consultants, who have access to computer programs for solving the appropriate equations speedily.

3.2 Venturi Tubes

The venturi tube, often known as the venturimeter, is the original form of differential pressure meter. (Strictly speaking, the 'venturi tube' is the primary device and the name 'venturimeter' refers to the combination of primary and secondary—but many users do not speak strictly!) A typical design is shown in *Figure 3.2*. Because energy losses are low and the flow conditions are not far removed from the ideal, the discharge coefficients of venturimeters are generally very near to unity, 0.98 being a typical value. *C* is, however, a function of Reynolds number, especially at low values of Re_D.

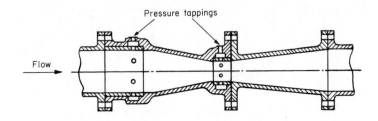

Figure 3.2 *Venturi tube*

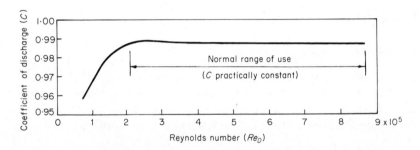

Figure 3.3 *Typical characteristic of a venturimeter*

A characteristic curve obtained from calibrating a typical venturi tube is given in *Figure 3.3*. The coefficient falls off sharply at low Reynolds numbers, and venturi tubes are normally used only within the range where *C* is practically constant.

Various ways of modifying the venturi tube so as to make it more compact

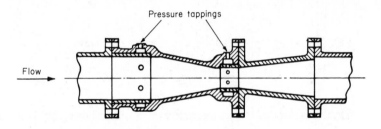

Figure 3.4 *Truncated (or short) venturi tube*

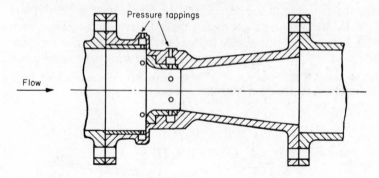

Figure 3.5 *Venturi nozzle*

without greatly impairing its performance are in use. In the truncated venturi
tube *(Figure 3.4)* the downstream cone is shortened, while in the venturi nozzle
(Figure 3.5) the contraction is shortened as well.

3.3 Orifice Plates

3.3.1 General Principle

An orifice plate is simply a plate with a hole in it, forming a partial obstruction
to the flow. As will be seen from *Figure 3.6*, the flowing fluid follows the same
kind of path as it does in a venturi tube. However, the narrowest part of the flow
stream is not in the orifice itself, but some distance downstream; this narrowest
section is known as the *vena contracta*. Between the vena contracta and the pipe
wall, numerous eddies form. These dissipate a great deal of kinetic energy in the
form of heat and are responsible for the high head loss of this type of meter.

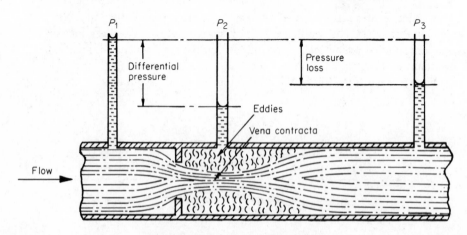

Figure 3.6 *Principle of the orifice plate*

Because the diameter of the vena contracta cannot be measured, orifice plate calculations are always based on the diameter of the orifice. This practice leads to very low values of C for orifice plates, in the region of 0.6.

3.3.2 Concentric Orifice Plates

Most orifice plates are made with a circular orifice concentric with the pipe. Even so, there is considerable scope for variation in the geometry of orifice-plate meters, and especially in the positioning of the pressure tappings, and in the shape of the upstream edge of the orifice.

In the typical orifice-plate installation of *Figure 3.7*, the tappings are in the adjacent pipes at distances of one pipe diameter D upstream and $D/2$ downstream. Another common arrangement is to put the tappings in the pipe flanges adjacent to the orifice plate. If these are drilled radially they are known as flange tappings; if drilled obliquely so as to enter the pipe right by the orifice plate, they are termed corner tappings. The position of the tappings affects the discharge coefficient and account is taken of this in the predicted values of C given in the standards.

The orifice plate of *Figure 3.7* is described as 'square-edged' because that is the shape of its upstream face, although the less significant downstream edge is chamfered. This is much the commonest form for orifice plates, being almost universally used with clean gases and clean liquids of low viscosity. With viscous liquids, however, it is necessary to make the *downstream* edge of the orifice square and the upstream edge either radiussed or chamfered; the former is termed the quarter-circle orifice plate, and the latter the conical-entry orifice plate. These devices have a fairly constant value of C at Reynolds numbers between about 5000 and 50 000.

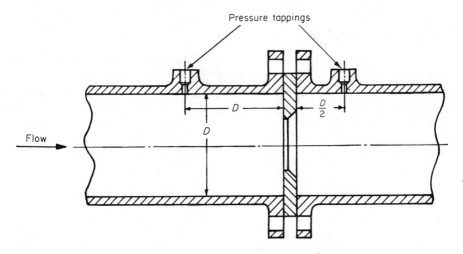

Figure 3.7 *Square-edged orifice plate with D and D/2 tappings*

The discharge coefficients of orifice plates are liable to vary with Reynolds number rather more than those of venturi tubes, but, with a plate made and used in accordance with the standards, C should not vary by more than about ±0.5% over the normal working range.

3.3.3 Eccentric and Chord Orifice Plates

Concentric orifice plates cannot be used with dirty fluids because dirt would gradually build up behind the plate until its performance was seriously impaired. Instead, eccentric or chord orifice plates *(Figure 3.8)* are commonly used. These are, in general, rather less accurate than concentric orifice plates but, because there is a free path along the bottom of the pipe, solids cannot accumulate behind the plate to any serious extent. Annular orifice plates, which consist of a solid circular disc supported centrally in the pipe, have also been used for this purpose but are rarely employed nowadays.

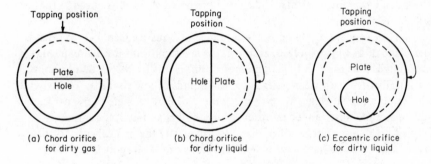

Figure 3.8 *Chord and eccentric orifice plates*

3.3.4 Integral Orifice Plates

Some manufacturers offer a compact unit comprising an orifice plate with a differential pressure sensor and signal transmitter built in. These assemblies are known as integral orifice plates. They are normally available for the smaller pipe sizes only.

3.3.5 Orifice Plates with Bypass Flowmeters

If, instead of the usual differential pressure transducer, a small flowmeter is connected across the pressure tappings of an orifice plate, the result is a metering system with special properties. These devices are dealt with in section 5.8.

3.4 Nozzles

Nozzles can be used in two quite different ways: as differential pressure meters for liquids and gases; or as sonic (critical) velocity regulating and metering devices for use with gases only.

3.4.1 Nozzles as Differential Pressure Meters

Nozzles designed to be used as differential pressure meters are illustrated in *Figure 3.9*. They are more costly than orifice plates but have three advantages over them: they have a discharge coefficient very much closer to unity; they can be used to discharge directly into the atmosphere; and they have no sharp edge to become blunted (*see* section 3.6f), so that they can be used with dirty and abrasive fluids.

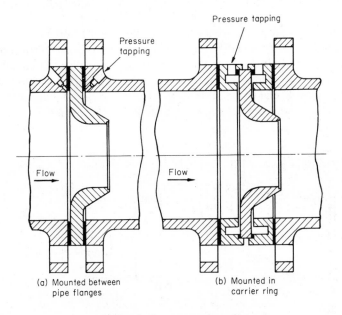

(a) Mounted between   (b) Mounted in
    pipe flanges   carrier ring

Figure 3.9 *Two types of nozzle*

3.4.2 Sonic Nozzles for Gas Flow

Provided the pressure drop across a nozzle is sufficient to ensure that the gas reaches sonic velocity in the throat, that velocity will be maintained within very close limits, and hence the (constant) volumetric flowrate through the nozzle can be calculated accurately. Although the volumetric flowrate through a given nozzle cannot be altered, the *mass* flowrate can be varied within fairly wide limits by varying the gas pressure and hence the density of the gas. If the nozzle is connected on the downstream side to a gradually tapered expansion, the resulting device is known as a sonic venturi-nozzle; much of the upstream pressure is recovered in the tapered expansion, so that the total head loss in the sonic venturi-nozzle is quite small.

The principal use of sonic nozzles and sonic venturi-nozzles is in the calibration of other types of gas meter[3,4] (*see* section 11.2.4).

3.5 Proprietary Low-Loss Differential Pressure Meters

By various ingenious modifications of the basic venturimeter geometry, it is possible to produce devices with an even lower head loss than an ordinary venturi. A number of proprietary devices of this type are available.

The two most widely used are probably the Dall tube[5] *(Figure 3.10)*, and the Universal venturi *(Figure 3.11)*. Others include the Lo-Loss flow tube *(Figure 3.12)* and the elaborately engineered Elliott–Nathan flow tube[6] *(Figure 3.13)*, for which an outstanding performance is claimed. In the same family there are two modern resuscitations of a nineteenth-century idea, the twin-throat venturi[7] and the multi-venturimeter[8,9]. Low-loss modifications of the orifice plate or the nozzle include the Dall orifice *(Figure 3.14)* and the Epiflo[10] *(Figure 3.15)*.

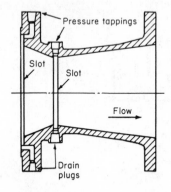

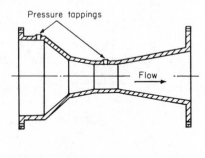

Figure 3.10 *'Dall' tube*   Figure 3.11 *'Universal' venturi*

The very low head loss of these devices is offset to some extent by their higher initial cost and, in some cases, by an increased sensitivity to upstream flow disturbances. Before buying one, it is worthwhile to ask the manufacturer for a guaranteed statement of its performance. This will facilitate the making of a simple cost-effectiveness analysis, to see whether the extra cost of the low-loss device justifies its use rather than a standard differential pressure device in your particular application.

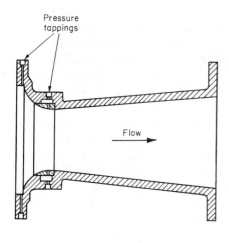

Figure 3.12 *'Lo-Loss' flow tube*

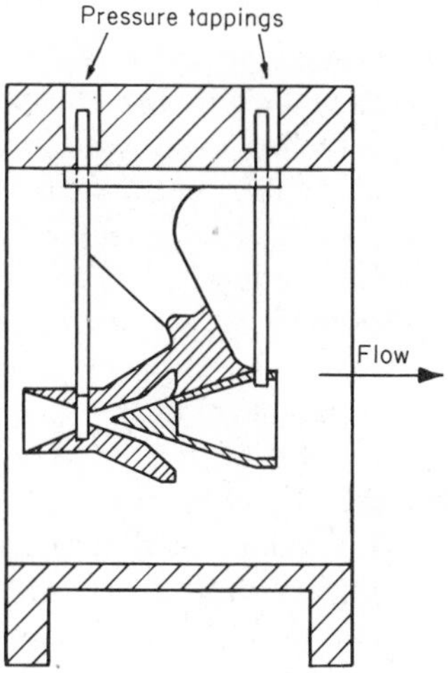

Figure 3.13 *'Elliott–Nathan' flow tube*

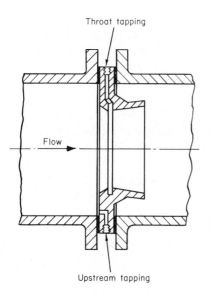

Figure 3.14 *'Dall' orifice*

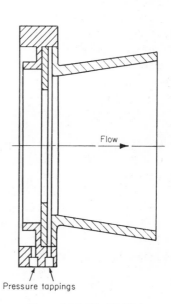

Figure 3.15 *The 'Epiflo'*

3.6 Points to Watch When Using

(a) It is all too easy to install an orifice plate back to front, thereby causing it to give erroneous readings for ever after. Remember that most orifice plates have the square edge on the upstream face, but conical-entry and quarter-circle plates have the square edge on the downstream face.

(b) When installing a differential pressure meter in a horizontal pipe, take care to have the pressure tappings in an acceptable position. These must never be in the bottom of the pipe where they would be liable eventually to clog with dirt. With liquids, the tappings are not usually sited at the top of the pipe either, since here they would be likely to fill up with air bubbles; the best place is generally at the side of the pipe, or in the case of a piezometer ring (*see* section 12.1.1) of four tappings, in the 45° position. Even then one must expect traces of air to get into the tappings; an air bleed is always provided somewhere in the pressure tubing, and it is essential that this should be used from time to time so that the occasional air bubble is cleared away.

(c) Stay within the recommended range of flowrates for the meter, since the stated coefficient of discharge may not apply outside this range.

(d) Remember that cavitation must not be allowed to occur within the meter; this can easily happen at high flowrates if the downstream pressure is too low (*see* section 10.3). Symptoms of cavitation may be a hissing or crackling sound, the presence of numerous air bubbles in the bleeds, and abnormal behaviour of the meter at high flowrates. If in any doubt about this, it is worth consulting the manufacturer or a flowmeter specialist.

(e) If a film of dirt, corrosion or organic growth gradually appears on the internal surface of a differential pressure meter or of the pipework immediately upstream, it will change the value of C and hence affect the accuracy of the meter. Make occasional inspections with this possibility in mind.

(f) Square-edged orifice plates are always manufactured with a sharp edge. After a few years' use, this may have worn enough to become blunt, and if so, its coefficient of discharge is likely to have increased significantly. (This danger is greatest where particles of abrasive solids are present in the fluids being metered, or with gases containing liquid droplets.) Where it is important to maintain the initial accuracy of an orifice-plate installation, the edge sharpness should be measured by an approved technique[11] at regular intervals—say, every five years if the fluid being metered is clean, or much more frequently if abrasive particles or droplets are present.

(g) When used with wet gases, orifice plates are often provided with a drain hole. This will affect the discharge coefficient slightly; take care to apply the appropriate correction.

3.7 Where to Learn More

In addition to the chapters on differential pressure meters in the general textbooks mentioned in Chapter 13, there is one useful book (now out of print) devoted to differential pressure meters[12], another to orifice plates[13], and another is concerned largely with differential pressure meters[14]; this last book is modestly priced and good value for money. For information on special types of differential pressure meter, the papers mentioned above are valuable[3-11].

The relevant British Standard[1] and ISO Standard[2] have already been mentioned. There is a useful extension to the British Standard dealing with the effects of deviating from the recommended practices[15]. Important American Standards on differential pressure meters have been published by the American Society of Mechanical Engineers[16], the American Petroleum Institute[17], the American Society for Testing and Materials[18] and the Instrument Society of America[19]. The corresponding German Standard is DIN 1952[20], an English translation of which is available from the National Engineering Laboratory[21]. There is also an ASME standard procedure for carrying out differential pressure meter computations[22], and an ISO Standard dealing with the connections between differential pressure meters and the associated differential pressure measuring devices[23]. Useful information on sonic venturi-nozzles has been published by Brain and Reid[24].

References

1 *BS 1042 : Part 1 (1964).* Methods for the measurement of fluid flow in pipes: Part 1–Orifice plates, nozzles and venturi tubes (revised edition due for publication shortly)

2 *ISO Standard 5167 (1978).* Measurement of fluid flow by means of orifice plates, nozzles and venturi tubes, installed in circular cross-section conduits running full

3 Hillbrath, H. S., 'The critical flow venturi: a useful device for flow measurement and control'. In R. B. Dowdell (Ed.), *Flow, its Measurement and Control in Science and Industry, Vol. 1, Part 1,* Instrument Society of America, Pittsburgh, 289–300 (1974)

4 Arnberg, B. T., Britton, L. L. and Seidl, W. F., 'Discharge coefficient correlations for circular-arc venturi flowmeters at critical (sonic) flow', *ASME Paper No 73-WA/FM-8,* American Society of Mechanical Engineers, New York (1973)

5 Miner, I. O., 'The Dall flow tube', *Trans. Am. Soc. Mech. Eng.,* 78, 475–479 (1956)

6 Lewis, D. C. G. and Singer, J., 'A new development in low loss metering'. In R. B. Dowdell (Ed.), *Flow, its Measurement and Control in Science and Industry, Vol. 1, Part 2,* Instrument Society of America, Pittsburgh, 501–506 (1976)

7 Kalinske, A. A., 'The twin-throat venturi: a new fluid flow measuring device', *J. Bas. Eng.* (Trans. ASME-D), 66 No. 3, 710–716 (1960)

8 Klomp, E. D. and Sovran, G., 'The fluid mechanics of multiple-venturi systems', *J. Bas. Eng.* (Trans. ASME-D), 94, No. 1, 39–45 (1972)

9 Klomp, E. D. and Sovran, G., 'A comparison of the multi-venturimeter to other low loss fluid meters', *J. Fluids Eng.* (Trans. ASME-I), 95 No. 1, 142–146 (1973)

10 Lewis, D. C. G., 'Further development of a low loss metering device based on the pressure difference principle'. In, E. A. Spencer and W. J. Ramsay (Eds.), *Fluid flow measurement in the mid 1970s,* HMSO, Edinburgh, 633–644 (1977)

11 Brain, T. J. S. and Reid, J., 'Measurement of orifice plate edge sharpness', *Measurement and Control,* **6** No. 9, 377–383 (1973) (Trans. Paper 17.73)

12 Anon., *Flow measurement by the differential pressure method,* 2nd edn., George Kent Ltd., Luton (1956)

13 Clark, W. J., *Flow measurement by square-edged orifice plate using corner tappings,* Pergamon, London (1965)

14 Anon., *Flowmeter Engineering Handbook,* 5th edn., Honeywell Automation, Fort Washington, Pennsylvania (1977)

15 *BS 1042 : Part 3 (1965).* Methods for the measurement of fluid flow in pipes: Part 3—Guide to the effect of departure from the methods in Part 1

16 Originally published as *Supplement to ASME Power Test Codes, Part 5,* Chapter 4, Flow measurement by means of thin plate orifices, flow nozzles and venturi tubes, American Society of Mechanical Engineers, New York (1959) (now superseded by *Fluid Meters,* ref. 7 of Chapter 13)

17 *Manual of Petroleum Metering Standards,* Chapter 14, Section 3, Orifice metering of natural gas (incorporating API 2530 and AGA Report No. 3), American Petroleum Institute in association with American Gas Association, Washington DC (1975)

18 *ASTM Standard D2458-69 (1975).* Flow measurement of water by the venturi meter tube

19 *ISA Standard RP 3.2 (1960).* Flange mounted sharp-edged orifice plates for flow measurement, Instrument Society of America, Pittsburgh

20 *DIN 1952 (May 1969).* Flow measurement with standard nozzles, orifice plates and venturi-nozzles (in German), Deutschen Normenausschusses, Berlin

21 *Mintech translation NEL TT 2192: DIN 1952 (May 1969),* National Engineering Laboratory, East Kilbride, Glasgow

22 *Flowmeter Computation Handbook,* American Society of Mechanical Engineers, New York (1961)

23 *ISO Standard 2186 (1973).* Fluid flow in closed conduits—connections for pressure signal transmissions between primary and secondary elements

24 Brain, T. J. S. and Reid, J., 'Operating characteristics of circular-arc critical flow venturis', *NEL Report No. 564,* National Engineering Laboratory, East Kilbride, Glasgow (1974)

4

Other Flowrate Meters Utilising Pressure Difference

What is this contraption of glass and brass?

Lord Curzon of Kedleston

There are many other flowrate meters which, although not qualifying as differential pressure meters, make use of pressure differences generated in flowing fluids. The most important types of these are described in this chapter.

4.1 Drag-Plate, or Target, Flowmeters

This meter is mentioned first because, of all the meters of this chapter, it is the one that most closely resembles a differential pressure meter.

4.1.1 How They Work

The principle of the drag-plate meter is illustrated schematically in *Figure 4.1*. A circular plate is supported centrally in the pipe by means of a hinged arm. The flowing fluid produces a positive pressure on the upstream side of the plate and a suction on the downstream side. This pressure difference produces a force which would tend to move the plate in the direction of flow, but this force is resisted by a null-balance supporting element at the end of the support arm. The signal from the null-balance device is proportional to the force on the plate, which in turn is proportional to the square of the flowrate.

The drag-plate consequently resembles an orifice plate turned 'inside out'— that is to say, the constricted flow passes through an annular opening near the wall of the pipe instead of through a hole at the centre. Moreover, the drag-plate can be regarded as its own differential pressure transducer, since the electrical output signal is a measure of the pressure difference across the plate.

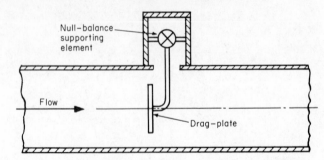

Figure 4.1 *Principle of the most common type of drag-plate flowmeter*

4.1.2 Advantages

(a) It shares with the segmental and eccentric orifice plates the important advantage that, because there is an unrestricted path along the bottom of the pipe, dirt cannot build up behind the plate; unlike them, however, it presents a symmetrical orifice to the flow and consequently has a better flow characteristic.

(b) There are no pressure tappings to become blocked with solid particles, gas bubbles (in liquid metering) or liquid droplets (in gas metering).

(c) It can be obtained with either pneumatic or electrical output signals.

(d) The flowrate range can be adjusted by a simple ranging switch (easy to perform, but of limited effectiveness), or by changing the drag-plate for a smaller or larger one (more effective, but involves a shutdown).

4.1.3 Disadvantages

(a) Like the orifice plate it has a square-root characteristic with consequently a limited rangeability.

(b) If good accuracy is required, it is necessary to use a reasonably small area ratio—that is to say, the diameter of the plate must be quite large in relation to the pipe diameter, and this creates a rather high head loss.

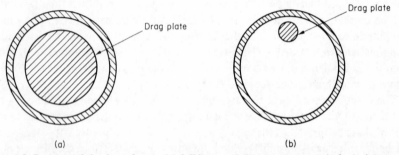

Figure 4.2 *Position of the drag-plate in (a) full-bore and (b) insertion-type (velocity) meters*

(c) The force on a large drag-plate would be too great to be supported effectively by a null-balance system. Consequently, the best known make of target meter is supplied only for pipes up to 100 mm diameter. (Another manufacturer supplies what he terms a target meter for pipe diameters up to 600 mm, but that device employs only a small drag-plate; it must therefore be regarded as a form of velocity meter or insertion meter (*see* section 7.8) and not a full-bore flowmeter. The essential difference between the two types is illustrated in *Figure 4.2.*)

4.1.4 When to Use Them

The drag-plate meter is particularly suitable for metering liquids containing suspended solids, and its use is largely confined to this special application.

4.2 Rotameters

4.2.1 How They Work

'Rotameter' is a word said to have been coined in Germany early in this century[1], to denote what would otherwise have to be called a 'variable-aperture (or variable-area) flowrate meter employing a vertical tube and a float' — hence the rapid worldwide acceptance of the name, which was subsequently adopted by a British company making this type of meter.

In the simplest type of rotameter the body is a tapered transparent tube of glass or plastic with a scale engraved upon it, as shown schematically in *Figure 4.3a*. Inside the tube is a small solid body with a circular cross-section; this is known as a 'float', although 'sinker' would be a more accurate description, since it is always denser than the fluid being metered.

When there is no flow the float rests at the bottom of the tube. Flow causes it to lift off its seat, so as to maintain the pressure drop across the float in equilibrium with the effects of buoyancy and gravity upon it. Since the immersed weight of the float is a constant for any given fluid, the pressure drop must also remain constant. Consequently, as the flow increases the float will rise in the tapered tube to provide a wider annular aperture for the fluid to pass through. The height of the float is thus an indication of the flowrate passing, and the scale on the transparent tube can be graduated directly in units of flowrate.

It is essential for the float to be maintained coaxial with the tube. This is normally achieved in the transparent-tube type of rotameter by the presence of inclined vanes on the float. The action of flow on these vanes imparts rotation to the float which provides the necessary stabilising and centering effect. It is this visible rotation which gave rise to the name 'rotameter', of course.

The broadly similar device shown in *Figure 4.3b* is also generally called a rotameter, even though it does not usually rotate. In this case the tube is made of metal and is not tapered, and the variable aperture is provided by the move-

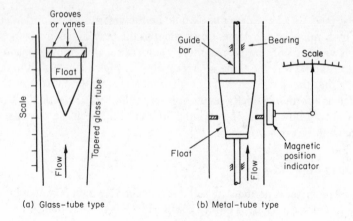

Figure 4.3 *The principle of the rotameter*

ment of a tapered float inside a fixed orifice. The position of the float is sensed
by an electromagnetic device on the outside of the tube, and its reading is
normally displayed on a dial, which may be either attached to the tube or remote
from it.

On the transparent-tube type the readout may be described as 'more or less
linear', since the vertical movement of the float is usually not too far from being
directly proportional to the flowrate. The metal-tube type allows scope for more
subtle engineering, and these are usually designed to give a truly linear characteristic. Both types have a rangeability of about 10:1.

4.2.2 *Advantages and Disadvantages of the Transparent-tube Type*

It is probably the handiest, cheapest type of flowrate meter on the market. Its
construction is so simple that there is very little that can go wrong with it unless
it is maltreated or used with unsuitable fluids; consequently it will usually
maintain its original performance for many years.

Against this must be set the fact that the performance of the cheaper versions
is never spectacular. To keep their price down they are normally given only a
rudimentary form of calibration, and their accuracy is then no better than ±2
or 3% at the full-scale reading. However, although they are not common, high-
precision glass rotameters can also be obtained—at a price—with an accuracy of
about ±0.5%.

The rotameter has quite a high head loss, and because it can only be used in
a vertical position it demands some contorted pipework if it is to be installed in
a horizontal pipe, which causes an additional head loss. Its readings are affected
by changes in viscosity or density, so that, for example, a meter intended for use
with water will be seriously in error if used with gasoline. It takes up rather a lot

of space, and, although models with a rather higher capacity are obtainable, it is rarely used for flowrates above about 1 litre of water per second, or a few tens of litres of air per second.

4.2.3 Advantages and Disadvantages of the Metal-tube Type

Because there is no risk of the tube bursting, the metal-tube rotameter can be used over a very wide range of temperatures and pressures, and large meters that will handle much higher flowrates than the transparent-tube type are practicable. If necessary it can be made from materials that will withstand acids and highly corrosive fluids, and designs with 'straight-through' connections are available which will handle viscous liquids and suspensions of solids. It can be supplied with either electrical or pneumatic readout.

Needless to say, these advantages have to be paid for, and the metal-tube rotameter generally costs much more than the glass-tube type. It also shares the latter's disadvantages of being rather bulky, of having a high head loss and of being sensitive to changes in viscosity and density.

4.2.4 When to Use Them

The inexpensive type of glass-tube or plastic-tube rotameter is often the most economical flowmeter for use where moderate or low flowrates of water, air or low-viscosity fuels have to be metered to within a few per cent. It is widely used both as a 'plumbed-in' flowmeter in process plants, and as a portable flowmeter for odd jobs in laboratories and test houses. The more costly high-precision glass-tube rotameter is useful as a reference meter.

The metal-tube rotameter has an entirely different sphere of usefulness. Its *forte* is handling awkward fluids which cause trouble with many other types of flowmeter, including viscous suspensions of solids in liquids. Although it can also be used with such simple fluids as air and water, it is unlikely to be the most cost-effective type of meter in such circumstances.

4.3 Spring-Loaded Variable-Aperture Flowmeters

4.3.1 How They Work

In the differential pressure flowmeter, the area of constriction is kept constant and the pressure difference which it creates is allowed to increase with flowrate. In variable-aperture flowmeters of the rotameter type, the reverse effect occurs: because it is balanced by the weight of the float the differential pressure is kept constant, whilst the area of the aperture is allowed to increase with flowrate.

The spring-loaded variable-aperture meter is, in effect, a hybrid between these two. A spring is used to press together the two members forming the variable aperture, so that, as flowrate increases, both the aperture *and* the force tending to close the aperture—and hence the differential pressure across it—must increase together. This means that the flow through this type of flowmeter possesses two degrees of freedom—a property which appears to be unique amongst high-precision flowrate meters. It accounts for these meters being unusual in another respect also: they have an outstandingly wide rangeability.

Two fundamentally different types are possible: firstly, those in which the displacement of the member controlling the aperture provides the readout, and secondly, those in which the readout is the differential pressure across the aperture.

Meters of the first type have been in use since the beginning of the century, and several such meters differing greatly in detail are offered by various manu-

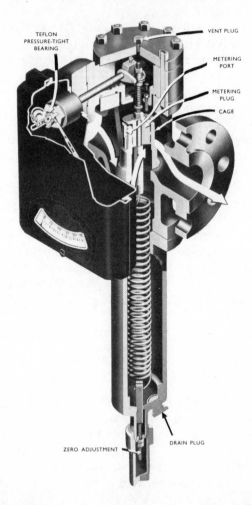

Figure 4.4 *The 'Miniline' spring-loaded meter (photo: Babcock Controls Ltd.)*

facturers today. One well known member of this class is the 'Miniline', shown in *Figure 4.4*. It may be regarded as a spring-loaded valve of the plug-and-port type, fitted with a system of levers and pneumatics for transmitting the motion of the plug to an external indicating dial and/or a remote recording station. Like most meters in this class it is bulky, and this limits its use to liquid flowrates of not more than a few litres per second.

The other type, in which the readout is differential pressure, is a fairly recent innovation. There appears to be still only one member of this class on the market, the 'Gilflo', one version of which is shown in *Figure 4.5*. It amounts to a spring-loaded needle valve, with tappings to enable the pressure drop across the valve to be measured. A very important feature is that the needle is deliberately profiled to produce a truly linear relationship between differential pressure and flowrate. It can be used with both liquids and gases, and being simpler in design than most other spring-loaded meters it can be made in sizes suitable for very high flowrates without being excessively large.

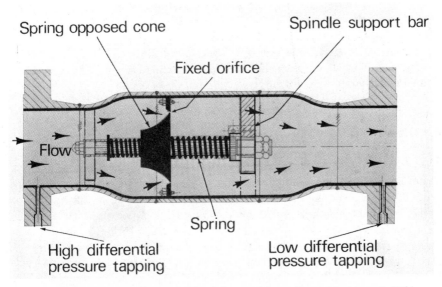

Figure 4.5 *The 'Gilflo-B' spring-loaded meter (photo: Gervase Instruments Ltd.)*

4.3.2 Advantages

(a) The prime advantage of a well designed spring-loaded meter is its exceptionally wide rangeability, tolerable accuracy being obtainable over a flowrate range of at least 20:1.

(b) The best meters of this type have a linear output over the whole of their working range.

(c) They tend to be less sensitive to viscosity changes than most other types of flowmeter and are therefore especially suitable for metering heated heavy fuel oil and other viscous liquids.

(d) Some types can be installed with their axis horizontal, vertical or inclined.

4.3.3 Disadvantages

(a) Like all variable-aperture flowmeters, they are larger in diameter than the pipes in which they are installed.

(b) They are rather expensive.

(c) They produce a high head loss.

4.3.4 Points to Watch When Buying

(a) Do you really need one or both of their two outstanding characteristics—wide rangeability and ability to deal with viscous liquids? If not, another type of meter may serve your purpose equally well at lower cost.

(b) The performance of spring-loaded meters from different manufacturers varies greatly. Ascertain from the manufacturer what accuracy he will guarantee in the intended installation and over what range of flowrates this applies; the limits within which the meter is linear; and the period for which it can be used before recalibration is needed.

4.4 Other Types of Variable-Aperture Flowmeter

The two most useful types of variable-aperture meter—rotameters and spring-loaded meters—have been described in detail. It is worth noting that several other types exist. Some of them are obsolescent, while others are still on the market.

The most useful of these is probably the swinging-flap type, of which the Kent 'Waste-Detecting' water meter is a well known example. In this, an orifice with its plane vertical is closed by a heavy flap which hangs from a hinge at the top. With increasing flowrate the flap opens until the gravitational forces are balanced by the differential pressure acting upon it. The angle of opening is then a measure of the flowrate; it is indicated through a mechanical linkage to a pen recorder. Advantages of this meter are very wide rangeability, moderate cost and simplicity. Disadvantages are non-linearity and moderate accuracy.

4.5 Laminar Flowmeters

4.5.1 How They Work

In turbulent flow, pressure drop is always proportional to the square of the velocity, and hence to the square of the flowrate. This is the reason for the unfortunate non-linear characteristic of differential pressure flowmeters and their consequent low rangeability.

With laminar flow, nature has been much kinder to the engineer, since here the pressure drop is directly proportional to the flowrate—a situation which immediately suggests the possibility of constructing a differential pressure meter with a linear output. The snag is that laminar flow can be obtained only in very narrow passages, or in tubes of extremely small diameter, and this imposes a severe practical limitation.

The simplest laminar flowmeter on the market consists of a single length of fine capillary tube with a highly sensitive differential pressure micromanometer connected across it. This will handle only very low flowrates: a typical single-capillary laminar flowmeter has a full-scale capacity of 0.5 cm^3 min^{-1}, and its principal use is as a leak-detector.

Much higher flowrates could be obtained by using a very large bundle of capillary tubes in parallel, but this would prove extremely expensive. In practice, small bundles of capillaries may be used for somewhat higher flowrates, but for substantially higher flowrates a honeycomb system is generally used. A section of one such honeycomb is shown in *Figure 4.6.*

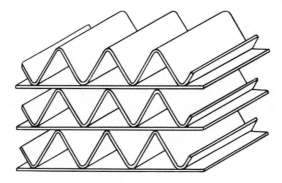

Figure 4.6 *Portion of honeycomb used in one type of laminar flowmeter*

For practical reasons laminar flowmeters are only used with gases. Models capable of handling up to about one standard cubic metre per second are available. One manufacturer supplies a device termed a 'compensator' which, when coupled to the differential pressure manometer, enables the operator to read the flowrate directly without having to perform any calculations.

4.5.2 Advantages

(a) Their output is approximately linear with flowrate (but not exactly so because of turbulent effects at the ends of the capillaries).

(b) Wide rangeability.

(c) No moving parts to wear.

(d) Will handle extremely low flowrates.

4.5.3 Disadvantages

(a) They are relatively bulky and expensive, especially the models designed for the higher flowrates.

(b) Their calibration is easily upset by dust particles settling in the capillaries and fine filtration of all gases being metered is therefore essential.

(c) They are highly sensitive to changes in the viscosity of the gas being metered.

(d) There is always the possibility that they might 'go turbulent' under some conditions of use and hence give false readings, although an alert operator should be able to foresee and avoid this danger.

4.6 Where to Learn More

The meters described in this chapter have received scantier treatment in the recent literature than most other types of flowmeter. This is probably because hardly any of them appear to have been standardised, so that almost every manufacturer pursues his own course and proprietary models abound; such a situation does not encourage scientific study. The notable exception to this generalisation is a series of standards on rotameters published by the Instrument Society of America[2]. From the meagre selection of other publications available I have selected the following as most likely to be useful.

The most exhaustive discussion to date of the properties of the drag-plate meter is probably the thesis by Hunter[3]; the paper by Hunter and Green[4] is much shorter but easier to obtain. The construction and theory of rotameters and some other types of variable-aperture meter have been discussed at length by Linford[5]. The theory of spring-loaded meters with differential pressure readout has been dealt with briefly by Turner[6] and in more detail by the writer[7]. A theoretical and experimental study of a single-capillary laminar flowmeter has been reported by Kawata et al.[8].

References

1 Linford, A., *Flow measurement and meters*, 2nd edn., Spon, London, 244 (1961)

2 *ISA Standards RP 16.1, 2, 3 (1959); RP 16.4 (1960); RP 16.5 (1961); RP 16.6 (1961)*

3 Hunter, J. J., 'An investigation into the static and dynamic characteristics of the drag-plate flowmeter', Ph.D. Thesis, Salford University (1974)

4   Hunter, J. J. and Green, W. L., 'Blockage and its effect on a drag-plate flowmeter'. In E. A. Spencer and W. J. Ramsay (Eds.), *Fluid flow measurement in the mid 1970s,* HMSO, Edinburgh, 173-193 (1977)
5   Linford, A., *Flow measurement and meters,* 2nd edn., Spon, London, 235-270 (1961)
6   Turner, D., 'A differential pressure flowmeter with linear response'. In C. G. Clayton (Ed.), *Modern developments in flow measurement,* Peregrinus, London, 191-199 (1972)
7   Hayward, A. T. J., 'A linear orifice-plate flowmeter', *J. Phys. E,* **9,** 440-442 (1976)
8   Kawata, M., Kurase, K., Yoshida, K. and Utsumi, H., 'Laminar flow and pressure drop in capillary tube'. In R. B. Dowdell (Ed.), *Flow, its Measurement and Control in Science and Industry, Vol. 1, Part 1,* Instrument Society of America, Pittsburgh, 17-26 (1974)

5

Rotating Mechanical Meters

One man's meter's another man's poison.

Author unknown

This chapter is concerned with rotating mechanical flowmeters of the 'full-bore' type, for measuring either the total volume or the volumetric flowrate of a fluid flowing in a pipe. Rotating mechanical devices used for measuring velocity at a point are dealt with in Chapter 7, and those used for mass flow measurement in Chapter 8.

5.1 Positive Displacement Meters for Liquids

5.1.1 How They Work

Until comparatively recently liquids being sold had to be measured by hand, using standard containers. Older readers will probably remember the days when a milkman who was asked for three pints would fill and empty a one-pint measure three times in succession. The first liquid quantity meters were the outcome of an attempt to mechanise this technique and thus turn it into an automatic, continuous process.

Such meters are usually known as positive displacement meters, although there is a tendency nowadays to drop the word 'positive' and call them displacement meters. In principle they all have the same mode of operation, in that they separate the flowing stream into a series of discrete 'pockets' of liquid and then count the pockets. However, in practice they achieve this end by a remarkable variety of means.

By way of example, three different types—a two-rotor gear meter, an oval-wheel meter and a sliding-vane meter—are illustrated diagrammatically in *Figure 5.1.* Many other types are in use, including three-rotor gear meters, multiple-piston meters, ring-piston meters and nutating-disc meters. They are all quite complex mechanisms, and it is beyond the scope of this book to describe their construction in detail.

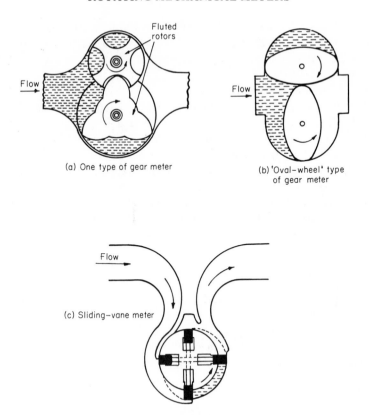

(a) One type of gear meter

(b) 'Oval–wheel' type of gear meter

(c) Sliding–vane meter

Figure 5.1 *Simplified schematic arrangements of three representative types of positive-displacement meter*

These are all examples of high-quality positive displacement meters, which are expensive products of precision engineering with a high accuracy. Their main use is for metering expensive liquids such as fuels and oils for the purpose of sale, although they are also used for many other purposes. There are other, cheaper, types of meter employing the positive displacement principle which are used for less exacting duties such as domestic water metering; they are dealt with in section 5.6. The present section is concerned solely with the high-quality types, for which the term 'positive displacement meter' is often reserved.

These highly engineered positive displacement meters are very nearly true to their name: the total volume of liquid displaced in one revolution of the meter is almost constant over a fairly wide range of flowrate, viscosity, pressure and temperature, so that the total number of revolutions of the meter provides a reasonably direct, or 'positive' measure of the total volume passed.

The big problem in designing any kind of positive displacement meter is to achieve good sealing of the moving parts without creating an unacceptable friction torque. The result is usually a compromise—a meter with a moderate

amount of friction torque and a moderate amount of liquid 'slip' through the
meter. For this reason every positive displacement meter needs to be calibrated
at several flowrates over the range within which it is to be used, with a liquid
of appropriate viscosity.

Most positive displacement meters are fitted with a totalising dial, reading
directly in litres or gallons. The readout mechanism often includes an adjusting
device, so that if, on calibration, the meter is found to be over-reading or under-
reading, it can be reset to read correctly. If the meter is subject to legal control,
this device will generally be sealed by the official inspector.

In addition to the usual dial for visual reading, some positive displacement
meters can be fitted with electrical pulse generators for use with remote recording
systems. Automatic temperature compensators (*see* section 12.4) are another
optional extra frequently found on these meters. They are also sometimes fitted
with an extra dial giving an approximate indication of flowrate.

5.1.2 Performance Characteristics

Like all complicated mechanical devices a positive displacement meter has a
frictional resistance to movement, and it takes a fair amount of energy to rotate
it. This energy has to be supplied by the flowing liquid, which loses quite a lot
of head in doing so. At extremely low flowrates there is insufficient energy in
the liquid to turn the meter at all; instead, the liquid slips slowly through the
fine clearances inside the meter, while the meter registers zero flow.

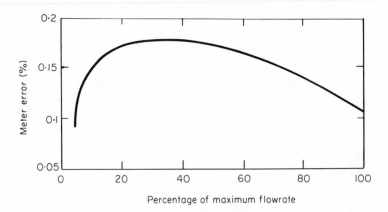

Figure 5.2 *Performance curve of a sliding-vane meter*

Nevertheless, in a well designed meter, slip is not a serious problem at flowrates within the normal working range. A performance curve for a vane-type
meter tested at NEL is given in *Figure 5.2,* where the great increase in slip at
low flowrate accounts for the rapid change in meter error within this region.

Despite this, the meter still has a rangeability of about 20:1, with a linearity of ±0.05% and an accuracy (when newly calibrated) of ±0.2% of volume over this range—a performance which cannot be matched by any flowmeters outside the positive displacement family. (Nor can it easily be equalled by other positive displacement meters; this particular type of meter is at, or very near, the top of its class.)

In general, positive displacement meters perform best when in the medium size range, that is to say, when designed for a maximum flowrate between about 2 and about 50 litres per second. Design limitations make it difficult to achieve high performance in either very small or very large positive displacement meters.

At present, the only way to obtain high performance from very small positive displacement meters is to fit them with a drive mechanism powered by an external servo-controlled motor. In this way, friction is practically eliminated, slip is minimised, and wide rangeability is obtained[1]. These highly sophisticated devices, however, are extremely expensive.

5.1.3 Advantages

(a) High-quality positive displacement meters will measure total liquid volume with high accuracy over a wide range of flowrates, and are very reliable over long periods. (For these reasons they are used exclusively in such applications as filling-station petrol pumps.)

(b) They will meter moderately viscous liquids accurately as long as they are calibrated with the right liquid, and in some models the dials can be adjusted to read correctly with the liquid concerned.

(c) The direct dial readout makes for simplicity of operation, enabling them to be used by unskilled operators.

(d) They are not affected by upstream flow disturbances, and so can be installed very close to a bend without loss of accuracy.

5.1.4 Disadvantages

(a) They are bulky, especially in the larger sizes.

(b) They have a high head loss (though not quite so high as is often supposed).

(c) They are viscosity-sensitive—but to a lesser extent than many other types of meter.

(d) They can be damaged by dirt particles, and filtration of the inflowing liquid is therefore usually necessary.

(e) The more accurate types are rather expensive.

(f) If they should seize up (a rare occurrence) they completely block the flow.

(g) They are suitable over only a limited range of pressure and temperature.

(h) Some types will introduce pulsations into the flow.

5.1.5 *Points to Watch when Buying and Using*

(a) Because there are so many different designs on the market, different manufacturers' products vary quite widely in performance. If you need good performance, it is well worthwhile obtaining certified performance curves from several suppliers for comparison, before deciding which meter to buy.

(b) These meters will normally work with the flow travelling in one direction only. Consequently, they are generally supplied with a choice of 'left-hand' or 'right-handed' dials. But there is no need to be dismayed if you have one with the dial facing in an inconvenient direction, because it is usually not difficult to remove the measuring head and rotate it through 180°.

(c) Never use a high-quality positive displacement meter with water without first checking that the internals are made from non-corrosive materials; such meters are usually termed 'water compatible'.

5.2 Positive Displacement Meters for Gases

5.2.1 *How They Work*

In principle, positive displacement meters for gases should be similar to those used for liquids as described in section 5.1.1 above, and share their advantages and disadvantages. However, in practice there is one very important difference. The energy in a flowing fluid is proportional to its density, and this means that a gas cannot easily supply sufficient power to operate a complex mechanical meter. Consequently, positive displacement meters for gases have to have a very low frictional resistance; and this requirement leads to some interesting variations in design.

The main types of positive displacement meter for gases are described separately, below.

5.2.2 *The Roots Meter*

The proprietary Roots meter is, in effect, a gear-type meter in which low frictional resistance is obtained by using lightweight meshing rotors of figure-of-eight shape[2], as shown schematically in *Figure 5.3*.

Its performance curve, *Figure 5.4*, follows the familiar pattern of positive displacement meter curves, with slip at low flowrates causing a sudden fall in the curve. The rangeability is around 20:1, with good linearity over most of this range. Accuracies of ±0.5% can be obtained.

Meters of this type can be obtained to cover flowrates up to $2 \, \text{m}^3 \, \text{s}^{-1}$ and pressures up to 80 bar, although they are rarely used at pressures above 10 or 20 bar because of the great weight of high-pressure models. The performance is little affected by upstream flow disturbances or distorted velocity profiles[3], but

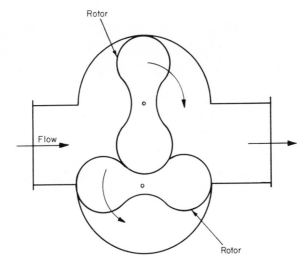

Figure 5.3 *Schematic arrangement of 'Roots' meter*

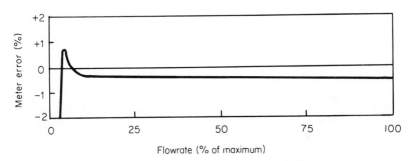

Figure 5.4 *Typical performance curve for a 'Roots' meter*

the Roots meter is adversely affected if severe pulsations are present in the flow reaching it[4].

Its main drawbacks are that it introduces cyclic pulsations into the flow, and that it cannot tolerate dirt, so that filters must be installed upstream.

5.2.3 The CVM Meter

The CVM is another proprietary gas meter of the positive displacement type. It is illustrated schematically at two stages in its operating cycle in *Figure 5.5*. It consists of a set of four vanes rotating in an annulus about a centre, A, and a gate rotating about a centre, B, which is so shaped that it will allow the vanes to pass but not the gas.

Its performance is broadly similar to that of the Roots meter except for the advantage that such pulsations as it may generate are usually of small amplitude.

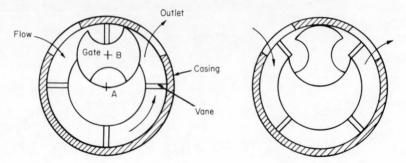

Figure 5.5 *'CVM' meter at two stages in its operating cycle*

5.2.4 Diaphragm Meters

The diaphragm (or bellows) meter is a simple, inexpensive and reliable meter of
moderate accuracy, widely used as a domestic gas meter[5]. It is included in this
chapter because it is a positive displacement meter, even though the only part
that rotates is the readout mechanism.

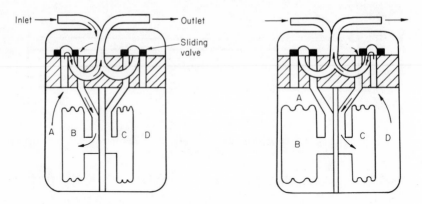

Figure 5.6 *Diaphragm meter at two stages in its operating cycle*

It can be regarded as a kind of four-piston reciprocating meter, in which two
bellows (B and C of *Figure 5.6*) act as two of the cylinders, and the annular
spaces around these bellows (A and D) as the other two cylinders, with the
operation being controlled by a double slide valve. In the first position shown
in *Figure 5.6,* A is emptying while B is filling, whereas C has just finished emptying and D has just finished filling. In the next position, C is filling and D is
emptying, whilst A has just been emptied and B has just been filled. A mechanical
linkage enables the number of cycles to be counted on a series of dials, which are
set to read in units of volume.

If this type of meter is fully calibrated and reasonably well maintained (conditions which are not necessarily fulfilled in domestic gas metering) an accuracy of ±1% over a flowrate range of 20:1 is feasible. Instruments suitable for flowrates up to 0.1 m^3 s^{-1} can be obtained, but this type of meter is limited to pressures and temperatures near to ambient.

5.2.5 Wet Gas Meters

The wet gas meter is probably the only type of positive displacement meter where the problem of sealing the moving parts without friction is fully solved without recourse to an awkward compromise. This remarkable feat is achieved by using a bath of water to provide the seal, as shown in *Figure 5.7*. The result is the most accurate gas volume meter known, with accuracies as good as ±0.25% over a flowrate range of 10:1 being claimed.

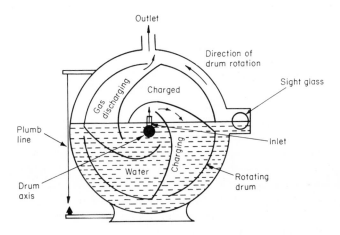

Figure 5.7 *Principle of the wet gas meter*

But there is a high price to be paid for this accuracy. The speed of rotation of the drum must be kept very low to avoid any significant disturbance of the water level. This means that the wet gas meter also holds the record for being the bulkiest flowmeter in existence. For example, a meter with an internal volume of around 0.5 m^3 cannot safely be used at flowrates above about 0.005 m^3 s^{-1}.

The instrument needs a highly trained operator, because great care must be taken if its full potential as an accurate meter is to be realised. One pitfall to be avoided is supplying this type of meter with dry air; since the air leaving a water-filled meter is liable to be saturated with water vapour, the operator must ensure that the incoming air is also saturated. Alternatively the meter may be filled with a suitable oil instead of water, in which case humidity problems should not arise, unless the oil is allowed to become wet. The liquid level inside the meter is critical: it must be maintained within close limits, and the meter must always stand level.

The main use of the wet gas meter is as a reference standard for calibrating other types of meter.

5.2.6 Servo-driven Meters

A promising newcomer to the field of positive displacement gas meters is a servo-driven oval gear meter[6]. As explained in the last paragraph of section 5.1.2 above, servo drive is an effective but expensive way of overcoming the friction/ leakage problems in positive displacement meters.

Although this meter is bulky and expensive, tests are said to have shown that accuracies of ±0.25% over a flowrate range of 50:1 can be obtained. Meters capable of handling up to 0.03 m^3 s^{-1} at pressures up to 15 bar were available in 1977.

5.3 Turbine Meters for Liquids

5.3.1 How They Work

'Turbine meter' is the name given to one particular type of rotating flowmeter. It consists of a short length of pipe in the centre of which there are two bearings supported by spiders. A propeller, large enough to fill the cross-section of the pipe almost completely, is mounted so that it can spin freely on these central bearings, as shown in *Figures 5.8* and *5.9*. Either the propeller blades are themselves made of magnetic material or a small magnet is inserted in the tip of each blade, and their passage past a pick-up mounted in the wall of the pipe causes electrical pulses to be emitted. If these pulses are passed into a pulse counter the total count is an indication of the total volume which has been delivered through the turbine meter, and if they are passed into a frequency analyser the frequency is an indication of the volumetric flowrate.

Large meters rotate more slowly, and hence they tend to have a lower pulse generation rate. If a higher frequency of pulse generation is required, they may be fitted with multiple pick-ups or with a shroud ring containing a number of magnets. Also, electronic pulse-multipliers are beginning to be used for this purpose, but it has not yet been shown conclusively that their accuracy is anything like that of the older methods.

The installation of three pick-ups in one meter has an additional advantage: their output can be used to check whether spurious pulses (from electrical interference) are being collected. For this purpose, the outputs from two of the pulses are fed, additively, into one counter, and the output from the other pick-up into a second counter. If the count on the first counter is double that of the

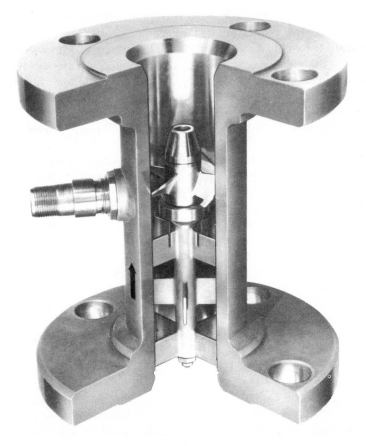

Figure 5.8 *Cutaway model of one type of turbine meter (photo: Foxboro-Yoxall Ltd.)*

Figure 5.9 *The internals of a typical turbine meter (photo: George Kent Ltd.)*

second, this means that all is well; but if it is significantly less than double, then electrical interference may be inferred (*see* section 10.9).

The weakest spot in a turbine meter is still the bearing, even though modern bearing materials give much less trouble than those of a few years ago. The bearing always has to support the weight of the rotor, and in some turbine meters the bearing also has to support some of the end thrust caused by the drag of the flowing liquid on the blades, although this thrust is taken up hydrodynamically in the best designed turbine meters. In large turbine meters the size of the bearing is quite small in comparison with the size of the meter, and errors arising from bearing friction become relatively insignificant; in very small turbine meters, however, bearing friction and geometrical effects can lead to considerable inaccuracies.

Other design parameters affecting turbine meter performance include the size of hub, the clearance between blade tip and pipe wall, and the shape, size and spacing of the blades.

The performance of a turbine meter cannot be predicted very accurately from hydrodynamic theory. Consequently, it is necessary for each individual turbine meter to be calibrated, so that the relationship between the number of pulses emitted and the volume of fluid passed can be determined experimentally. This results in a calibration curve of the form shown in *Figure 5.10*. A turbine meter is said to have 'linear output' over the range A–B in *Figure 5.10*, where the volume of liquid passing through the meter is almost exactly proportional to the number of pulses emitted. The meter becomes inaccurate and cannot be used to give reliable results at flowrates less than those corresponding to the point A, because at these lower flowrates bearing friction becomes too great to be tolerated. At flowrates higher than those corresponding to the point B, the meter becomes unusable because of fluid effects such as excessive hydro-dynamic drag and cavitation.

For metering liquids such as milk, turbine meters are available which can easily be taken to pieces for cleaning. Another special form of turbine meter is

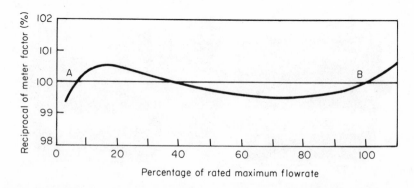

Figure 5.10 *Performance curve of a typical turbine meter for liquids*

the bi-directional type, for use in pipes where the flow is liable to be reversed on occasions.

5.3.2 Advantages

(a) Turbine meters of sizes above about 50 mm, and especially the very large sizes, have excellent short-term repeatability. If they are recalibrated at fairly frequent intervals they can be extremely accurate.

(b) Their output is directly digital and, in the best meters of this type, is practically linear over a fair range of flowrates—about 5 or 6:1 in the smaller sizes, increasing to about 10:1 in large turbine meters.

(c) They produce only moderate head loss.

(d) They are compact, being only the same diameter as the pipe in which they are installed.

(e) The compactness of the smaller sizes of turbine meter, combined with their freedom from any components necessitating a hole in the pipe wall, enables them to be designed for operation at very high pressures.

(f) If they should seize up, they do not block the flow.

5.3.3 Disadvantages

(a) They are rather more expensive than many types of flowmeter, particularly in the larger diameters.

(b) A turbine meter cannot maintain its original calibration over a very long period, because this is bound to change gradually with wear or fouling of surfaces, and periodical recalibration is therefore necessary if high accuracy is to be maintained. Bearing problems are more likely to occur with liquids of poor lubricating quality, and their effect with liquids containing a high proportion of suspended solids or with highly corrosive liquids can be serious.

(c) The calibration characteristic of a turbine meter is sensitive to changes in the viscosity of liquid being metered. The effect of viscosity is very great in small turbine meters, becoming progressively less serious as the size of meter increases. With oil, or any other viscous liquid whose viscosity is likely to change with small changes in temperature, it is difficult to obtain high accuracy without installing a calibration device such as a pipe prover (*see* section 11.1.5) to enable the meter to be recalibrated rather frequently under the actual conditions of use; this is a common practice in the petroleum industry.

(d) They are sensitive to flow disturbances, and especially to the presence of swirl.

(e) The very small sizes do not perform as well as their big brothers, because of the relatively greater importance of bearing friction in small meters.

5.3.4 *Points to Watch when Buying*

(a) The turbine meter is a high-quality device intended mainly for applications where accurate measurement of flowrate and/or total quantity is needed, and especially for metering large quantities of petroleum and its products. Does your application justify the use of this rather costly type of meter?

(b) Examine the calibration curve supplied by the manufacturer. Is the meter linear to within ±0.25% over a suitable range of flowrates?

(c) Is the meter certified as suitable for use with the fluid for which it is intended, and at the anticipated pressure and temperature?

(d) Does the meter have straight blades or helical blades? Straight-bladed meters appear to be less affected by variations in velocity profile, but helical-bladed meters are generally less affected by variations in viscosity.

5.3.5 *Points to Watch when Using*

(a) Because your turbine meter has been designed for use with liquids, never blow out the line in which it is installed with compressed air or steam, since this would probably cause it to overspeed and serious damage can result.

(b) If dirty liquids such as crude oil are being metered, it is essential to protect the meter by installing a coarse filter or strainer upstream of it.

(c) Power cables, motors, switchgear, etc., produce electromagnetic radiation. This can be picked up by the pulse counter, causing it to over-read. To avoid such errors, follow the advice in section 10.9.2, and *see* also the third paragraph of section 5.3.1.

(d) Make sure there is sufficient pressure in the line to avoid cavitation, installing a back-pressure valve if necessary. The standard codes of practice (*see* section 5.10) and manufacturers' handbooks give the necessary figures. Remember that hydrocarbons cavitate more readily than water, so that higher back-pressures are generally needed with oils and fuels.

(e) Follow the standard practice with regard to the required length of straight pipe upstream and downstream, and install a flow straightener if necessary (*see* sections 10.1 and 10.2).

(f) If the meter is to be calibrated *in situ* against a pipe prover, make sure that the prover is connected downstream of the meter, not upstream.

5.4 Turbine Meters for Gases

5.4.1 *How They Work*

These meters operate on the same principle as turbine meters for liquids, as described in section 5.3.1. Because of the relatively low kinetic energy of a flowing gas, however, it is necessary to make a significant difference in shape. A turbine meter for gases, as shown in *Figure 5.11,* always has a rotor with a large central hub. This causes the flowing gas to accelerate through the meter,

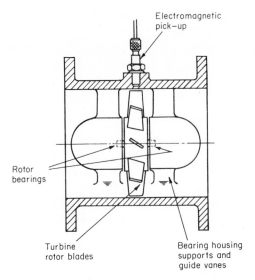

Figure 5.11 *Turbine meter for use with gases*

and to concentrate its impelling force on the blades near the perimeter, where they will generate the maximum possible torque.

In addition, the bearings have to be designed to run·for long periods in air with very little friction. Some meters are made with aerostatic bearings, but conventional low-friction mechanical bearings appear to be more widely used at present.

Because of the increased relative importance of bearing friction, turbine meters for gases are rather less linear than liquid turbine meters, as is shown in

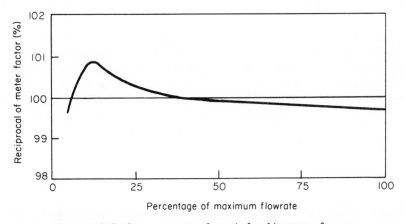

Figure 5.12 *Performance curve of a typical turbine meter for gases*

Figure 5.12. In the larger sizes they give highly repeatable readings, and maintain their accuracy over quite a long period of time.

Some turbine meters for gases are fitted with a mechanical readout system, through a gear train. Because of the extra friction imposed, these do not have quite the same performance as those with an electrical pick-up.

5.4.2 Advantages and Disadvantages

They share the advantages and disadvantages already attributed to turbine meters for liquids (sections 5.3.2 and 5.3.3), except that they are rather less sensitive to upstream disturbances[7,8] and that they are practically insensitive to changes in the viscosity of the gas being metered. The latter is a significant advantage, since it means that they do not need the very frequent recalibration required by turbine meters used for the metering of oil at high accuracy levels.

5.4.3 When to Use Them

Their main sphere of usefulness is in the accurate metering, for purposes of sale or taxation, of large volumes of natural gas and gaseous chemicals at moderate or high pressure. In this field they are beginning to challenge the long-established supremacy of the orifice plate, because, although more expensive, they offer better accuracy and rangeability than the orifice plate.

5.5 Miniature Pelton Wheel Meters

5.5.1 How They Work

This useful newcomer to the field of liquid flow measurement is now being offered by several manufacturers. Although it bears only a superficial resemblance to a true Pelton wheel, the name 'Pelton wheel meter' is used for want of a better one. The meter affords a means of measuring low liquid flowrates more easily and perhaps more accurately than can be done by any other flowmeter giving a direct digital output. It achieves this by concentrating the incoming liquid into either one or several small high-velocity jets, which impinge tangentially on the periphery of a free-spinning rotor. The rotation of the rotor is monitored by an electromagnetic or photoelectric pick-up; the frequency of the resulting electrical pulses indicates flowrate, and their total number is a measure of the total volume flowing.

The cheapest and simplest devices of this type employ a light-weight rotor suspended on jewelled bearings, and a single jet. The more elaborate version shown in *Figure 5.13* splits the incoming flow so that a series of tangential jets striking the rotor around its periphery are used to suspend the rotor by hydro-dynamic forces, thus eliminating the need for a bearing.

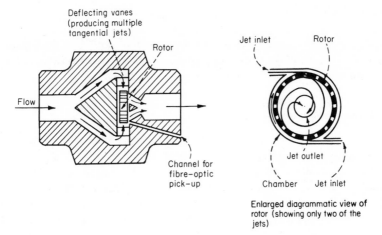

Figure 5.13 *Principle of the bearingless multi-jet 'Pelton-wheel' flowmeter*

5.5.2 *When to Use Them*

They are worthy of consideration whenever low liquid flowrates have to be measured and a pulsed electrical output is required. In this area they may well prove both more accurate and less costly than a small turbine meter.

5.6 Mass-Produced Total-Volume Rotary Meters

So far we have looked at rotary flowmeters of types which can be neatly classified. However, there are a great many other mechanical meters which almost defy classification, since about all that they have in common is a rotating member of substantial size which revolves at a speed roughly proportional to the flowrate, and a mechanical system for recording the total output on dials. The rotor may take the general form of a propeller or axial-flow turbine, or of a vane-wheel with the flow impinging tangentially at one or more points, or the meter may be some simple form of positive displacement meter. Great variations in detail of all these broad types are possible.

Such meters are suitable for mass production at a moderate price and, when they take this form, they cannot be expected to have more than a moderate performance. Although they are sometimes useful in a general engineering situation, their main use is as domestic or industrial water meters, domestic fuel oil meters, and similar situations where low initial cost and good reliability are more important than high accuracy. (To make life more complicated, one occasionally comes across a precision-engineered meter of one of these types, with a higher performance and a correspondingly higher price than its mass-produced counterpart. Before buying one, compare its price and performance with that of high-quality positive displacement meters and of turbine meters.)

5.7 Some Other Rotary Flowmeters

There are still other types of rotary meter which cannot easily be classified, some of which partly overlap the mass-produced category mentioned in the previous section. Three types of particular interest will be described below.

5.7.1 Constrained-vortex Meters

The constrained-vortex meter, sometimes known simply as a vortex meter, must not be confused with the vortex-*shedding* meter (*see* section 6.3), with which it has nothing in common. As shown in *Figure 5.14,* the constrained-vortex meter consists of a large, freely spinning rotor mounted with its axis perpendicular to the flow path, which is eccentrically placed in a bulge in the pipe. Various designs are offered by different manufacturers, but most commonly an external mechanical readout system is driven by the rotor through a magnetic coupling, which eliminates the need for sealing a drive-shaft. Electrical pulse generators are usually an optional extra.

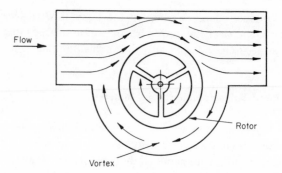

Figure 5.14 *Principle of the constrained-vortex meter*

These meters offer a cheaper but less accurate alternative to positive displacement and turbine meters. Designs for both liquids and gases are available. The former are sometimes used with 'difficult' liquids, because their simplicity of construction promotes good durability and they can fairly easily be dismantled for maintenance. They are also sometimes used with viscous oils, since their accuracy is said to be less affected by viscosity changes than is the case with turbine meters; this property is probably the consequence of the high degree of turbulence which they generate.

5.7.2 The 'Hoverflo'

The Hoverflo was originally described by its inventor as a 'turbine flowmeter without bearings'[9], but its manufacturers now call it a 'bearingless turbine *type* transmitter'. This is a better description because this meter neither looks like a turbine meter nor behaves like one.

As shown in *Figure 5.15,* the Hoverflo is rather like a double rotameter, with the two floats joined together by a rigid shaft, and each taking half the main flow. When flow is passing the rotor takes up a central position which is one of stable equilibrium, and thus it floats without any metal-to-metal contact. This still applies even if the meter is installed in a vertical pipe. A magnetic pick-up provides a direct digital output.

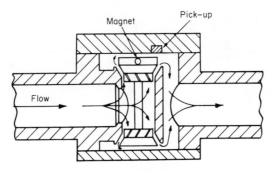

Figure 5.15 *Schematic arrangement of the 'Hoverflo'*

This meter does not set out to compete with conventional turbine meters, and cannot match their performance on simple liquids. Its linearity is only moderate, so that an accuracy of ±0.5% can be maintained over a range of only about 3:1, although the rangeability can be extended to 10:1 if a lower accuracy can be tolerated. In addition, it is rather sensitive to viscosity changes.

Nevertheless, this meter does fill what was previously a gap in the market. Its bearingless action, coupled with the clean lines of the flow path through the meter, enable the Hoverflo to cope successfully with all sorts of 'difficult' liquids that would probably foul up any other type of rotating meter, including liquids with abrasive particles in suspension.

5.7.3 The Angled Propeller Meter

The angled propeller meter *(Figure 5.16)* is an interesting hybrid between an insertion meter and a turbine meter.

An insertion meter (*see* section 7.8) is a small device which can only measure the fluid velocity at one point in a cross-section, and although the total flowrate can usually be inferred from such a measurement, the resulting value cannot be very accurate. A turbine meter, on the other hand, is large enough to be affected by all the flow at a cross-section and therefore gives a very much more accurate indication of total flowrate. But it will only work with liquids that are clean, because its bearings have to be in the flow path and thus are adversely affected by dirt particles suspended in the liquid.

Figure 5.16 *The angled propeller meter (photo: B. Rhodes and Son Ltd.)*

The angled propeller meter, while having a rotor large enough to be affected by practically the whole flow passing, has its bearings outside the flow stream where they are rather less likely to be damaged. Moreover, because it enters the main pipe through a branch pipe, it can easily be removed in a few minutes for maintenance, without breaking any of the main pipe joints. It has a rangeability of about 10:1, although its accuracy and linearity are only moderate over this range. Where moderately 'difficult' or dirty liquids have to be metered with moderate accuracy at a moderate cost, this meter is worth considering.

5.8 Bypass Meters

5.8.1 How They Work

Bypass meters, often known as shunt meters, go back a long way. Not very long after differential pressure meters came into use somebody tried connecting a small mechanical flowmeter across the pressure tappings instead of a manometer, as shown in *Figure 5.17,* and received a pleasant surprise. The flowrate in the bypass was an approximately constant fraction of the flow in the main pipe.

This interesting result arises because the relationship between flowrate and pressure drop in the bypass follows a square law, and this cancels out the square-root effect in the orifice plate itself. In this way, the bypass effectively turns the differential pressure meter into an approximately linear meter, and at the same time provides a simple way of integrating its output to give total volume.

One snag lies in the phrase 'approximately linear output'. To obtain something

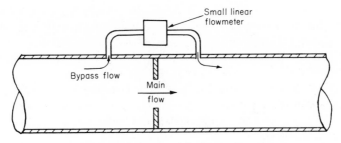

Figure 5.17 *Principle of the bypass flowmeter*

like true linearity, very careful design of the whole system is needed. For this reason, home-made bypass metering systems are not of much practical use, and a variety of purpose-built bypass meters is on the market.

5.8.2 Some Practical Designs

The 'Kent Rotary Shunt Meter' was developed in the 1920s and is still widely used today for metering total quantity of steam, water, compressed air and industrial gases[10]. The simple design shown in *Figure 5.18* could be used with liquids, but to make the meter suitable for use with gases a damping vane is

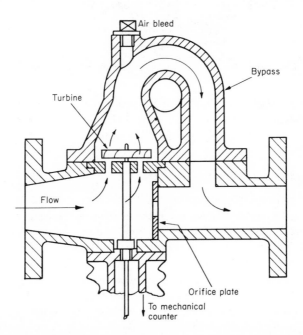

Figure 5.18 *Simplified arrangement of the 'Kent Rotary Shunt Meter'*

fitted on the output shaft. The basic bypass meter is made in 2-, 3- and 4-inch
sizes, whilst for larger pipes the bypass meter is itself used to bypass an orifice
plate, thus creating a composite 'bypass to a bypass' type of meter.

A newcomer to the field of bypass meters is known as the 'Metre Meter' linear
digital orifice plate[11]. This utilises a single-jet miniature Pelton wheel meter
(*see* section 5.5) which is sufficiently small to be incorporated within the body
of the orifice plate, thus making an extremely neat and compact device
(Figure 5.19). The readout is a series of electrical pulses, and a rangeability of
well over 10:1 is claimed.

Figure 5.19 *A compact form of bypass meter, the 'Metre Meter' (photo: Litre Meter Ltd.)*

Another commercially available system employs a rotameter as the bypass
meter[12]. This is convenient when only a visual indication of flowrate is required,
but lacks the totalising capability of the other systems.

5.8.3 Advantages and Disadvantages

The prime advantage of the bypass system is economy: it enables very large
flowrates to be measured with a small, inexpensive meter. In addition, several
bypass meters, including the rotary shunt meter and the linear digital orifice
plate, provide a simple means of totalising the flow. Bypass meters produce a
moderate head loss, and they usually have a nominally linear characteristic.

Their main disadvantage is that their linearity and accuracy are generally
inferior to those of more expensive meters. Nevertheless, they offer such a
large saving in cost that they provide an attractive method of measuring total
quantity and/or flowrate in medium-sized or large diameter pipes, in applications
where moderate accuracy is acceptable.

5.9 Metering Pumps

5.9.1 How They Work

A metering pump may be regarded as a combination of pump, flowmeter and flow regulator, all in one[13]. It usually consists of a piston pump with a variable stroke, a device for counting the number of strokes delivered and a presettable mechanism which will stop the pump when the required number of strokes has been delivered. Since the pump normally runs at a constant speed, the operator can preselect the required flowrate by choosing the correct length of stroke. Also, he can control the total quantity delivered by setting the mechanism to give the appropriate number of strokes.

Metering pumps should not be expected to run at less than one-tenth of maximum stroke—in other words, they have a rangeability of about 10:1. The amount they deliver at a given stroke is viscosity-dependent, and so they should be calibrated on the appropriate liquid if a reasonably high accuracy is required.

5.9.2 When to Use Them

Metering pumps have two main uses. First and foremost, they are devices for process control—a use which falls outside the scope of this book.

Second—and highly relevant to our subject—they may be regarded as flowmeters of the 'when-all-else-fails' category. They will handle highly viscous liquids, non-Newtonian fluids, molten polymers, and all sorts of horrible, sticky substances that would make any normal flowmeter die of fright. With such substances the measurement rule is simple: meter them if you can; but if you cannot, then pump them with a metering pump which has been previously calibrated with the operating liquid.

5.10 Where to Learn More

In addition to the references already quoted, and the relevant chapters in the general textbooks mentioned in Chapter 13, there are several important standard specifications, either published or pending, on the most widely used types of mechanical meters.

There are API standards on positive displacement meters[14] and turbine meters for liquids[15], both of which are shortly to be superseded by chapters of the new API Measurement Manual, which is mentioned in section 13.2.2. ISO recommendations on both these types of meter, as well as on mechanical mass-produced water meters, are in an advanced stage of preparation. There is also an ISA standard on turbine meters[16].

A useful state-of-the-art paper on turbine meters for liquids was published in 1977 by Watson[17]. There are several OIML Recommendations for positive displacement meters for use with liquids and gases[18-22], and publication of one on rotary water meters is pending. There are also EEC 'directives' (standards) for positive displacement meters[23], water meters[24], and gas meters[25].

References

1   Henning, H. J., 'Die messung kleiner Durchflussmengen', *MTZ Motor-technische Z.*, **29**, No 2 (1970)
2   Walker, R. K., 'A historical review and discussion on the design factors of positive displacement gas meters', *Instrum. Control Syst.*, **39** No 10, 141-143 (1966)
3   Thompson, R. J. S., 'Rotary positive displacement meters', Institution of Gas Engineers seminar on gas measurement, University of Salford, September 1969
4   Jeannon, J. M. and Cockrell, D. J., 'The causes, effects and suppression of pulsations from rotary positive displacement gas meter systems'. In E. A. Spencer and W. J. Ramsay (Eds.), *Fluid flow measurement in the mid 1970s*, HMSO, Edinburgh, 585-603 (1977)
5   Delaney, L. J., 'Rotary and diaphragm displacement meters', *Instrum. Control Syst.*, **35** No 11, 114-117 (1962)
6   Takado, A., 'Servo-driven oval gear meters', Proceedings of the 1977 International School of Hydrocarbon Measurement, at Oklahoma University, 440-448 (1977)
7   Jepson, P. and Bean, P. G., 'Effect of upstream velocity profiles on turbine flowmeter registration', *J. Mech. Eng. Sci.*, **11** No 5, 503-510 (1969)
8   Fenwick, J. S. and Jepson, P., 'The problems and needs in large volume gas measurement'. Paper presented at the conference 'Transducer 75', London, Trident Conferences Ltd. (1975)
9   Wemyss, W. A. and Wemyss, A. C., 'Development of the 'Hoverflo': a turbine flowmeter without bearings'. In E. A. Spencer and W. J. Ramsay (Eds.), *Fluid flow measurement in the mid 1970s*, HMSO, Edinburgh, 521-540 (1977)
10 Thurlow, S. R., 'Integrating total flow to an accurate degree—economically', *Technical Paper No 7209*, Kent Instruments Ltd., Luton (no date)
11 Wemyss, W. A., 'Discussion on a linear digital orifice plate', *Proc. Flow-Con. 77*, Institute of Measurement and Control, London, 149-154 (1977)
12 Gotthardt, W., 'High capacity bypass flowmeter', *Measurement and Data*, **Nov.-Dec.**, 80-83 (1976)
13 Woodcraft, G., 'Metering pumps: versatile machines for process control and regulation', *Process Eng.*, **May**, 80-85 (1973)
14 *API Standard 1101 (1965)*. American standard method for measurement of petroleum liquid hydrocarbons by positive displacement meter
15 *API Standard 2534 (1970)*. Measurement of liquid hydrocarbons by turbine meter systems

16 *ISA Recommended Practice, ANSI/ISA RP 31.1 (revised edn. 1977).*
Specification, installation and calibration of turbine flowmeters
17 Watson, G. A., 'The application of turbine meters to present day flow
metering requirement', *Proc. Flow-Con. 77,* Institute of Measurement and
Control, London, 89–137 (1977)
18 *OIML Recommendation IR 5.* Meters for liquids other than water with
measuring chambers
19 *OIML Recommendation IR 27.* Meters for liquids other than water—
complementary devices
20 *OIML Recommendation IR 6.* Gas meters—general
21 *OIML Recommendation IR 31.* Gas meters with deformable walls
22 *OIML Recommendation IR 32.* Gas meters with rotary pistons and
turbine meters
23 *EEC Directive OJ 7/26/71.* Meters for liquids other than water
24 *EEC Directive OJ 1/20/75.* Cold-water meters
25 *EEC Directives OJ 9/6/71 and OJ 7/12/74.* Gas volume meters

6

Other Volumetric Flowmeters

It's clever, but is it art?

Rudyard Kipling

6.1 Electromagnetic Flowmeters

6.1.1 How They Work

The electromagnetic flowmeter utilises the same basic principle as the electrical generator: when a conductor moves across a magnetic field a voltage is induced in the conductor, and the magnitude of the voltage is directly proportional to the speed of the moving conductor. If the conductor is a section of conductive liquid flowing in a non-conductive pipe through a magnetic field, and electrodes are

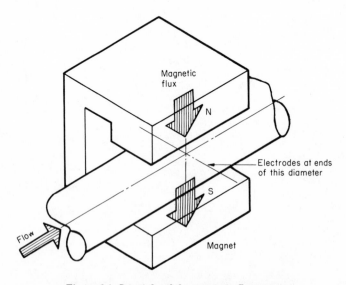

Figure 6.1 *Principle of the magnetic flowmeter*

mounted in the pipe wall at the positions shown in *Figure 6.1,* the voltage induced across the electrodes should be proportional to flowrate.

In such a situation, provided that the velocity profile is symmetrical and the magnetic field is uniform over a fairly long section of the pipe, a simple mathematical analysis reveals that

$$U = B\bar{v}D \tag{6.1}$$

where U is the induced voltage, B is the magnetic flux density, $\bar{v}$ is the mean velocity of flow, and D is the pipe diameter.

In reality magnetic fields are not completely uniform and flow profiles are not perfectly symmetrical. For this reason the exact mathematical analysis of practical electromagnetic flowmeters is extremely difficult, and if high accuracy is to be obtained from them they need to be calibrated just like any other flowmeter.

There are also a number of practical problems which have to be taken into account in designing these meters, and so high-quality electromagnetic flowmeters are a great deal more complex than the simple situation of *Figure 6.1* might suggest.

The main difficulties are as follows.

(a) At practical flow velocities the value of the induced voltage is very small and hence difficult to measure accurately, especially if 'stray' voltages are not completely eliminated.

(b) Mains voltage and frequency are never completely stable, and unless the circuit is designed to compensate for these input fluctuations they will give rise to spurious output fluctuations.

(c) Ordinary direct current cannot be used to power the electromagnets without causing polarisation of the electrodes, but if (as was always the case until fairly recently) ordinary alternating current is used, this causes a kind of transformer effect which generates troublesome out-of-phase voltages.

(d) It is difficult to obtain a completely stable electrical zero; in other words,

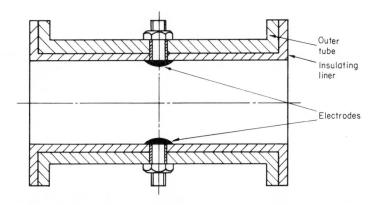

Figure 6.2 *Simplified plan view of flow tube for an electromagnetic flowmeter*

'zero drift' can be a serious problem, especially in the older types of electro-magnetic flowmeter.

(e) Some liquids quickly foul the electrodes, thereby causing the meter to give false readings unless remedial action is taken.

Complicated circuitry has proved necessary to deal with these problems. Recently it has been found that square-wave alternating current (sometimes known as pulsed direct current) provides a good way of dealing with problems (c) and (d). Built-in ultrasonic devices for cleaning the electrodes automatically are the most popular way of dealing with (e), although electrolytic cleaning or mechanical wipers are sometimes used instead.

The mechanical construction of a typical meter is shown diagrammatically in *Figures 6.2* and *6.3*. To avoid shorting the electrodes the meter has to have an insulating liner *(Figure 6.2)*. The field coils are sited at 90° from the electrodes and the whole assembly is, in this particular design, encased by a laminated yoke *(Figure 6.3)*. The selection of materials for the insulating liner and the electrodes is quite important, and it is usual for meters to be almost tailor-made for the particular liquid, temperature and pressure envisaged.

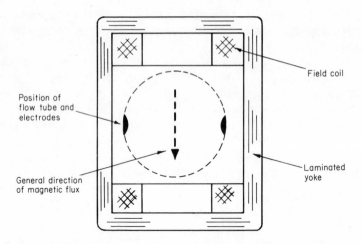

Figure 6.3 *General arrangement of one form of electromagnetic flowmeter (elevation)*

6.1.2 Advantages

(a) There is no obstruction whatever to the flow, and electromagnetic flow-meters are therefore well suited for measuring heavy suspensions, including mud, sewage and wood pulp.

(b) They have a zero effective head loss—which means that the loss is no more than that of the length of straight pipe which the meter replaces. This makes it a suitable meter for large water-supply pipelines, where low head loss is essential.

(c) Industrial electromagnetic meters are made over a wider range of sizes than almost any other type of meter, namely, from about 3 mm to about 3 m diameter.

(d) Electromagnetic meters are not too seriously affected by upstream flow disturbances, unless severe asymmetry of velocity profile is present.

(e) They are practically unaffected by variations in density, viscosity, pressure, temperature, and (within limits) electrical conductivity.

(f) Range-switching circuits are available which enable one meter to be used over a very wide range of flowrates (much more than the usual 10:1), although accuracies may be poor at the low end of a particular metering range.

(g) The output is essentially linear.

(h) These instruments are naturally bi-directional in operation and hence can be used for the measurement of reversing or pulsating flow, provided that the frequency of pulsation is well below the frequency of the magnetic field excitation.

(i) Special instruments for measuring the flow of some molten metals are available, although it may be necessary to go to a specialist manufacturer for these.

(j) Other highly specialised electromagnetic meters are made for measuring flow in human blood vessels.

6.1.3 Disadvantages

(a) The liquid to be metered must have a reasonable electrical conductivity. Just what constitutes 'reasonable' conductivity is a matter of controversy; electromagnetic meters can be built to cope with liquids having as low a conductivity as 0.1 μmho cm^{-1}, but these are highly sophisticated and costly devices. For ordinary industrial purposes the practical limit is more like 10 μmho cm^{-1}; this means that water-based liquids can be handled comfortably, but hydrocarbons and most other organic liquids cannot.

(b) Although modern electromagnetic meters are considerably better than those of a few years ago, they are still not among the most accurate of flowmeters. About the best accuracy obtainable today from the general run of electromagnetic flowmeters is ±1% over a flowrate range of 5:1, with accuracies falling off considerably at flowrates below 20% of full scale. A few manufacturers now offer super-quality meters with a claimed accuracy of ±0.5% over a 5:1 range, but these are expensive, and it remains to be seen whether such accuracies can be maintained over a long period in industrial service.

(c) The size and cost of the field coils and circuitry do not increase in proportion to the size of the meter; consequently, although large electromagnetic meters are undoubtedly good value for money, with decreasing pipe sizes the meters become relatively more and more bulky and expensive.

6.1.4 Points to Watch When Buying

(a) When comparing quotations, look at specifications and/or guaranteed accuracies as well as prices. For example, square-wave excitation costs more than ordinary alternating current input, but gives a better performance; it is a waste of money to pay for that extra performance if it is not really needed.
(b) Make sure that the meter you buy is suitable for the whole range of duty you have in mind for it.
(c) Is a built-in electrode-cleaning device needed?
(d) How has the meter been calibrated? The expression 'dry calibration' is a trade term meaning that the meter has not been calibrated at all, in the usual sense of the word; it describes the process of measuring the field strength and *deducing* the expected relationship between output and flowrate. For accurate results a proper calibration on a water test circuit is essential; this is known in the industry as a 'wet calibration'. The smaller sizes can be flow-calibrated over their whole working range, but calibrating very large meters presents a difficulty. They are often calibrated only over the bottom of their range, with the upper part of the calibration curve being extrapolated; this is a great deal cheaper but obviously less satisfactory than full-range calibration, which should be employed whenever it is economically possible.
(e) If the meter is to be installed below ground level—in a pit, for instance—make sure that the design is one which will withstand 'drowning'.

6.1.5 Points to Watch When Using

(a) Never take an electromagnetic meter which was bought for one kind of duty and employ it on some other duty without first checking that it is suitable—because there is a good chance that it will not be.
(b) Never install a meter with the electrodes at the ends of a vertical diameter, because the one at the top of the pipe would be affected by the occasional air bubble passing by.
(c) Follow exactly the manufacturer's instructions for connecting up the meter. If you fail to do this, electrical interference may cause the meter to give false readings.
(d) Check the zero of the meter occasionally when the flow is shut off. This is not so essential with modern designs as it used to be, but is still a sensible precaution to take with all meters.
(e) Make sure that the meter always runs full.
(f) If the meter is installed in a pipe where an electrogalvanic corrosion prevention system is in use, then electrical bonding straps must be used to bypass the currents around the meter.

6.2 Ultrasonic Flowmeters

6.2.1 Introduction

Ultrasound can be used in several different ways to measure the mean velocity or flowrate of a fluid in a pipe. The outcome of this is that the term 'ultrasonic flowmeter' may refer to any one of a number of widely different devices on the market today. Some types can be used with gases, but at present the great majority of ultrasonic flowmeters are used with liquids. (There are also some ultrasonic velocity meters available, which will be mentioned briefly in Chapter 7.) It will be necessary to deal with each of the main types in turn, and then finally to discuss the situations in which each type may be worth using.

The outstanding advantage of all types of ultrasonic meters is that they present no obstruction to the flow and cause no head loss, and yet their use is not restricted to conductive liquids as is the electromagnetic meter; also, there are no mechanical parts to wear.

6.2.2 The Single-path Diagonal-beam Meter

This meter was one of the earliest types of ultrasonic meter to come into operation, and is still quite widely used. It depends on the fact that a sound wave, just like a boat on a river, moves faster when travelling with the current than against it. In the design shown in *Figure 6.4* the difference in velocity between the upstream and downstream beams will depend upon the velocity of the flowing liquid, and will be practically unaffected by the velocity of sound in the liquid, since this will almost cancel out in the subtraction.

Modern meters of this type use only one pair of transducers and the upstream and downstream beams follow the same path, with the beams being transmitted in pulses so that each transducer can act as both transmitter and receiver alternately. Two different methods of measuring the velocities are in use, known as the 'sing-around' and 'leading edge' methods. Most meters claiming high

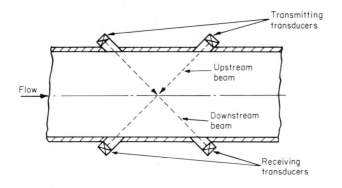

Figure 6.4 *Principle of the diagonal-beam ultrasonic meter*

accuracy now employ the latter method, which involves measuring the time of
flight of an ultrasonic pulse.

The main snag with this type of meter is that it measures the (unweighted)
mean velocity *across a diameter*—and this is not at all the same thing as the mean
pipe velocity, $\bar{v}$, which is a weighted mean, with most emphasis being given to the
velocities nearer to the pipe wall (where the majority of the liquid is) and very
little to those at the pipe centre. A calibration factor has to be applied to the
meter readout to allow for this important difference. So long as the meter is used
in a situation where the actual flow profile is identical with the profile where it
was calibrated, then it will read accurately. Unfortunately this can never be
guaranteed: even the effect of pipe wall roughness can change a flow profile
sufficiently to affect this type of meter to some extent, and swirl and asymmetry
arising from upstream disturbances can cause quite serious errors.

The single-path diagonal-beam meter must therefore be regarded as a reasonably priced flowmeter in the moderate accuracy class. It is doubtful whether the
accuracies of ±1% over a range of at least 20:1 claimed by some manufacturers
can be achieved in industrial practice, unless very great pains are taken to ensure
an almost perfect velocity profile.

Diagonal-beam meters perform best in pipes of fairly large diameter. The
practical lower limit of diameter for single-path diagonal-beam meters of good
accuracy is in the region of 100 mm.

6.2.3 The Multi-chordal Diagonal-beam Meter

The great disadvantage of the single diagonal beam can be largely overcome by
using, say, four-chordal paths, arranged as shown diagrammatically in *Figure 6.5*.
By integrating over four suitably spaced chordal paths it is possible to give almost
the correct weighting to the mean flow velocity thus derived.

In this way a meter very much less sensitive to variations in flow profile is
obtained. The multi-chordal diagonal-beam type is for this reason much the
most accurate type of ultrasonic flowmeter: accuracies in the region of ±0.5%
over a flowrate range of 10:1 are attainable today, and it is conceivable that

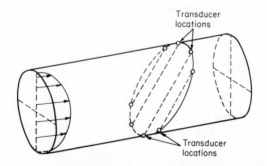

Figure 6.5 *Arrangement of transducers in a four-chordal diagonal-beam ultrasonic flowmeter*

future development could result in further improvement. It also happens to be by far the most expensive type, partly because of the cost of accurately position-ing four pairs of transducers, but mainly because some complicated computing circuitry is needed to carry out the signal processing. It seems likely, however, that current developments in the field of microprocessors will help to reduce the cost considerably.

Despite their high cost, meters of this type appear to have considerable potential for situations where large quantities of valuable liquids have to be metered to the highest possible level of accuracy over a long period. They are particularly attractive for use in large metering stations where a single data processor can be made to serve several meters, with a consequent great saving in the cost per meter. At the time of writing several governments are interested in their use for the fiscal metering of crude oil, for instance.

6.2.4 The Cross-correlation Ultrasonic Meter

The cross-correlation meter employs two transverse beams of ultrasound only a short distance apart *(Figure 6.6)*. When there is no flow, the two signals received are the same as those transmitted. However, when turbulent flow occurs the passage of an eddy (A, B, C, etc.) through a beam causes the signal to be modulated, and the exact shape of the modulation is like a fingerprint—it enables the particular eddy causing it to be identified, and so the eddy can be tracked as it travels downstream.

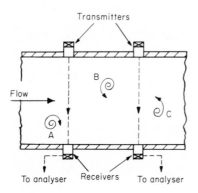

Figure 6.6 *Principle of the cross-correlation ultrasonic flowmeter*

By comparing the two received signals in a special data-processing unit known as a correlator it is possible, in principle, to detect the passage of individual eddies through two beams a known distance apart, and thus to ascertain their velocity. Practical meters are not able to give information on individual eddies, but are designed to give a mean value of the velocity of all the eddies across one

diameter. If there are no eddies present the meter may be made to track aggrega-
tions of dirt particles or air bubbles in the flow. If the flowing fluid is homogenous
and free from eddies, the cross-correlation meter will not work.

Like the single-path diagonal-beam meter this meter gives an incorrectly
weighted mean velocity, and is therefore prone to inaccuracy on account of
velocity profile variations (*see* the third paragraph of section 6.2.2). This puts it
in the moderate-accuracy category. It has one particular advantage which will be
discussed in section 6.2.6.

6.2.5 The Doppler-effect Ultrasonic Meter

The Doppler effect is familiar to everyone who has noticed the pitch of a siren
changing as the vehicle carrying it passes by. This is just one everyday illustration
of the principle that the frequency of a sound vibration emanating or reflected
from a moving object changes in frequency, and the magnitude of the frequency
change is proportional to the speed of the object.

The Doppler-effect ultrasonic meter works by measuring the velocity of dirt
particles or small air bubbles naturally occurring in the liquid. In *Figure 6.7*
ultrasound from a transmitter is reflected from dirt particles A, B, C, etc., and
picked up by a receiver, which in practical instruments is sometimes combined
with the transmitter. The receiver circuitry is designed to give a mean value of
the frequency shifts caused by many dirt particles, and hence a mean velocity.

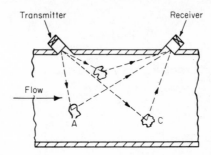

Figure 6.7 *Principle of the Doppler-effect ultrasonic flowmeter*

Once again the mean is not correctly weighted, and therefore the meter is
sensitive to flow profile variations (*see* the third paragraph of section 6.2.2) and
to the distribution of dirt particles in the cross-section. A further disadvantage is
that, unlike the other types of ultrasonic meter mentioned above, its readings
are affected by changes in the velocity of sound in the liquid, so that it is both
density-sensitive and temperature-sensitive. These problems make it unsuitable
for accurate measurement, but it has some compensating advantages which are
discussed below.

6.2.6 Built-in, or Clamped-on?

An ultrasonic beam will travel quite happily through the wall of a pipe. This gives the designer of ultrasonic flowmeters for liquids a unique advantage over other flowmeter designers: he is free to choose whether to mount his transducers integrally within the wall of a special piece of pipe (as in *Figures 6.4, 6.6* and *6.7*), or whether to put them in separate housings which the user can then fix on the outside of his existing pipework, by clamping or gluing. This method, however, will not work with gases. A typical clamp-on meter is shown in *Figure 6.8*.

Figure 6.8 *A clamp-on meter of the Doppler-effect type, with combined transmitter and receiver (photo: Ryaland Pumps Ltd.)*

The clamp-on option is very attractive to the user who wants to avoid the trouble and expense of breaking open his pipe for the installation of a flow-meter. But there is a rather heavy price to pay for this convenience, since clamp-on meters are bound to be less accurate. This is partly because their performance depends on the accuracy with which the user can set the relative positions of the transmitter and receiver, and partly because an ultrasonic meter measures a velocity; to convert this into a flowrate the user must multiply by the (estimated) area of the internal cross-section of his pipe.

The expensive and highly accurate multi-chordal diagonal-beam meter must be constructed to very close tolerances, and therefore is only available as a preformed unit with built-in transducers. Single-path diagonal-beam meters can be obtained either as preformed meters, with a claimed accuracy of ±1% over a range of at least 10:1, or as the less accurate clamp-on units. Both the cross-correlation and the Doppler-effect types are best suited to clamp-on operation, and are available commercially in this form. Of the two, the cross-correlation type is probably more accurate, although it has not been on the market long enough for its performance to be fully established, whilst the Doppler type is cheaper and more convenient.

6.2.7 Which Type for Which Job?

The high cost of the multi-chordal diagonal-beam meter is only justified where a meter of very high accuracy, repeatability and reliability is really necessary. Its other advantages (no obstruction, no head loss, linear output, wide range) are best regarded as side benefits, since they can be obtained more cheaply in other types of meter. Because its accuracy falls off much more sharply than its cost in the smaller pipe sizes, it is doubtful whether the use of sizes below about 250 mm diameter is economically justified.

Next in order of accuracy and cost comes the single-path diagonal-beam meter. In sizes of about 100 mm diameter and above, it is roughly comparable in performance with an electromagnetic flowmeter, except that on the plus side it will handle non-conducting fluids, and on the minus side it is more seriously affected by upstream flow disturbances and by pulsating flow. The smaller sizes are less accurate.

At the bottom of the accuracy table come the clamp-on meters. Where they score is in convenience, and there are many applications where this is more important than their absolute accuracy. Their repeatability is very much better than their absolute accuracy, which means that if you can devise some means of calibrating them *in situ* their accuracy can be greatly improved.

The easiest clamp-on meter to install is the type of Doppler-effect meter that employs only one transducer; this also avoids the problem of errors arising from the incorrect spacing of transducers, which occurs with every other type of clamp-on meter. However it will not work with very clean liquids, and like all Doppler-effect meters it is affected by changes in the temperature and the composition of the liquid. Where a simple, inexpensive, easily installed meter of very moderate accuracy is required, the clamp-on Doppler meter can be extremely useful.

6.3 Vortex-shedding Meters

6.3.1 How They Work

How do you make a band play if it is an elastic one? Easy—just take it in your two hands, stretch it in front of your face about an inch away from your lips, and then blow on it. When the relationship between the tension in the rubber

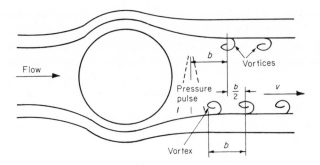

Figure 6.9 *Vortex shedding by a bluff body*

band and the air velocity is just right, the band will hum quite loudly.

This happens because a succession of fluid vortices is emitted from the trailing edges of a body placed across a flowing stream *(Figure 6.9)*. The only way to prevent this is by streamlining the body; conversely, the vortex-shedding effect can be enhanced by using what is known as a 'bluff body'—that is, something shaped as awkwardly as possible, such as a prism whose cross-section is a rectangle or a triangle with its apex pointing downstream. As *Figure 6.9* indicates, the vortices are emitted alternately from opposite sides of the obstruction with a distance b between adjacent vortices. In an ideal fluid their frequency, v/b, will be proportional to the fluid velocity. Associated with each vortex is what amounts to a pressure pulse, and so when the vortex-shedding frequency happens to equal the natural frequency of the obstruction it will resonate. Hence the noise emitted by your elastic band, whispering pines, and the Aeolian harp of the Greeks.

Within the past few years a considerable number of flowmeters employing this principle have appeared on the market. They all consist of a spool of pipe containing a bluff-shaped rod lying across one diameter, and some means of sensing the frequency of vortex shedding.

From there on, however, each manufacturer is on his own. They all seem to use different cross-sections for the bluff body, including a circle, rectangles,

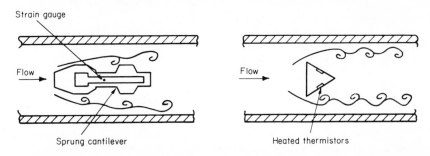

Figure 6.10 *The principles employed in two commercial vortex-shedding meters*

modified triangles, and other more complicated shapes. An almost incredible variety of frequency-sensing systems is already in commercial use. These include mechanically vibrating devices whose motion is detected by various means, including magnetic pick-ups, strain gauges, and capacitance sensors. Various non-mechanical frequency detectors are also used, including systems based upon ultrasonic beams, hot thermistors and hot films. Two commercial systems are shown schematically in *Figure 6.10*.

This bewildering variety is liable to give a potential purchaser a headache. Suggestions for dealing with the situation are made in section 6.3.3 below.

6.3.2 Advantages and Disadvantages

Vortex-shedding meters are aimed at much the same section of the market as orifice plates. The vortex-shedder has in general about the same moderate accuracy as the orifice plate (under favourable circumstances it can be more accurate), a similar head loss, and much the same sensitivity to upstream flow disturbances. As with the orifice plate, it is not necessary for every individual meter to be calibrated, since its flow characteristics can be predicted with reasonable accuracy. Like the orifice plate it has no rotating mechanisms to wear or break down, and it can be designed to operate with both gases and liquids, either clean or dirty.

There the resemblance ceases. The vortex-shedding meter scores over the orifice plate by having a linear output, a rather better repeatability, a much wider rangeability (10:1 is easily obtained and under favourable conditions this can be greatly exceeded) and a direct digital output. Moreover, if the cost of the associated differential-pressure transducer is added to that of an orifice plate, the vortex-shedder can actually be cheaper than the orifice plate in sizes below about 200 mm diameter. As the size increases, however, the vortex-shedder becomes progressively less competitive in price. Also, because the K-factor of vortex-shedding meters is inversely proportional to D^3, the pulse generation rate of large meters is so low that it is difficult to calibrate them accurately.

For vortex-shedding meters to give their optimum performance the flow must be well into the turbulent range. At pipe Reynolds numbers below about 20 or 30 000 their accuracy begins to fall off, and below about 3000 they become unusable.

6.3.3 Points to Watch When Buying

The widespread introduction of the vortex-shedding meter has been so sudden and so recent that there has not yet been time for the principle of 'the survival of the fittest' to operate. Some manufacturers' designs are bound to give a better performance than others, but it is difficult to go beyond that statement of the obvious. The position is far from static, since most manufacturers are still in the process of updating and perfecting their designs.

While this situation continues it behoves an intending purchaser to tread warily. When writing for quotations you should state precisely what you want the vortex-shedder to do; ask each manufacturer if his product will do it, and—especially—ask for the experimental evidence on which he bases his answer.

6.4 Some Other Non-mechanical Oscillatory Flowmeters

The vortex-shedder is only one example of a meter in which the fluid itself is made to do the oscillating, at a frequency proportional to the flowrate. There are several other ways of achieving the same end, two of which are in fairly general use and are therefore worthy of mention here. The first method has given rise to a whole family of basically similar devices known as fluidic meters, which are suitable only for small or moderate liquid flows (pipe diameters up to about 100 mm). The other is a proprietary instrument called the Swirlmeter, which is specifically for measuring gas flow. They both have a performance broadly similar to that of the vortex-shedding meter. Their mode of operation is described below.

6.4.1 Fluidic Flowmeters

As most engineers know, the term 'fluidics' describes the technology of control devices employing small fluid jets, which can be used for the purposes of switching, amplification and so forth, in ways which resemble the use of electronics. Such devices frequently make use of the Coanda effect, in which a jet of liquid adheres to a nearby solid surface.

In a bistable fluidic device the liquid jet can take up two alternative positions.

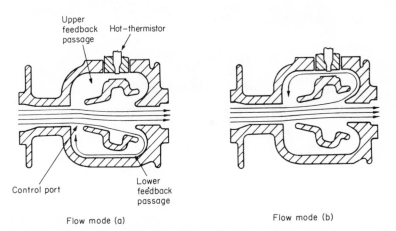

Figure 6.11 *Principle of operation of one type of fluidic flowmeter, shown with the flow in each of its alternative modes*

If some feedback circuitry is added which always tends to direct the jet away from its momentary position, this will cause it to oscillate between the two stable positions, at a frequency proportional to the jet velocity.

A number of liquid flowmeters based on bistable fluidic systems have been developed, but not all of them have reached the market. One which has is illustrated in *Figure 6.11*. In flow mode (a) the jet is caused by the Coanda effect to take up the lower of its two possible positions. However, in this position a small part of the jet is diverted around the lower feedback loop, and the small stream emerging from this loop is sufficient to deflect the jet into its upper position. This in turn initiates flow mode (b), where flow in the lower feedback passage ceases and flow in the upper feedback loop occurs instead, thus pushing the jet back to its lower position—and so on, *ad infinitum.*

The frequency of oscillation is detected by a hot-thermistor velocity sensor (*see* section 7.4) in one of the feedback passages.

Figure 6.12 *Cutaway model of a 'Swirlmeter', showing precession of centre of vortex (photo: Fischer and Porter Ltd.)*

6.4.2 The 'Swirlmeter'

This instrument for measuring the flowrate of gases is shown in *Figure 6.12*. The first thing the gas stream encounters on entering the meter is a device called a swirler, which resembles a turbine meter whose bearing has seized; this causes the whole of the gas stream to rotate as it continues along the pipe, with the axis of rotation being the centre line of the pipe.

Then the gas enters a venturi contraction, which makes it accelerate—and it is a principal of fluid mechanics that, when a rotating body of fluid accelerates, its axis of rotation follows a path shaped like an expanding helix. In the venturi throat the velocity becomes constant again, and the axis of rotation then follows a simple helical path. The passage of the coils of this helix is detected by a hot-thermistor velocity sensor, and the frequency of the pulsations emitted by this sensor is directly proportional to flowrate.

After passing the detector the flow enters an expansion which takes it back to the original pipe diameter, and finally a flow straightener removes most of the swirl before the flow leaves the meter.

6.5 Tracer Flowmeters

6.5.1 How They Work

Although tracer-type flowmeters are a fairly recent innovation, the underlying methods have long been in use for measuring the flowrate of rivers. There are two quite distinct methods, one of which depends on measuring the velocity of the tracer, whilst the other depends upon measurements of tracer dilution.

The tracer-velocity method is extremely simple. In its simplest form it makes use of naturally occurring tracers. For example, in measuring the flowrate of a river one could time the passage of several pieces of floating driftwood between two points a known distance apart, and then take their average speed as an approximation to the mean velocity of the river.

A more accurate result can usually be obtained by introducing an artificial tracer. This might take the form of a bucketful of concentrated red dye thrown into the centre of the river. As the dye travels downstream, turbulence will cause it to mix thoroughly with the water, so that it will gradually spread out to form a large red patch. If you make a judgement as to where the centre of this patch lies, its velocity will be a fairly close approximation to the mean velocity of the river.

The tracer-dilution technique is more elaborate. A concentrated tracer has to be injected at one point at a known flowrate, Q_1. Some distance downstream, where the tracer has had ample opportunity to mix thoroughly with the river, a number of samples of river water are taken, mixed together, and analysed to determine the concentration of the tracer in the water, c. It is fairly obvious that if this concentration is, say, one part in a thousand, the river flowrate will be

$1000\ Q_1$. Generalising, the flowrate of the river, Q_2, will be given by

$$Q_2 = Q_1/c \qquad\qquad (6.2)$$

(This analysis is a deliberate oversimplification to illustrate the method. The tracer substance may already be present in small quantities in the water, in which case its natural concentration must be measured and fed into a more elaborate version of equation 6.2.)

When either of these concepts is embodied in a flowmeter, the result is a tracer-type meter. Obviously, such a meter cannot rely upon injecting a dye or a chemical into a pipe—it must either make use of naturally occurring tracers, or it must inject a non-material tracer, such as heat or an electric charge. Even within these limitations, however, a wide variety of methods is possible, and tracer flowmeters of the following kinds are already in use.

(a) Dirt-particle velocity meters, employing ultrasonic Doppler-effect meters (already described in section 6.2.5) or laser–Doppler-effect meters (see section 7.7).

(b) Meters which use naturally occurring eddies as tracers, and measure their velocity by cross-correlating their modulating effects upon two ultrasonic beams (already described in section 6.2.4).

(c) Gas-ionisation meters. These employ a permanent radioactive source to ionise a gas flowing in a pipe, and an electrically charged grid to deionise it. Both ion-concentration and ion-velocity methods have been used.

(d) The nuclear-magnetic-resonance flowmeter.

(e) Thermal flowmeters.

Of these, (a) and (b), which are described in detail elsewhere in this book, are mentioned in this section only for the sake of completeness; (c) is not yet of sufficient industrial importance to warrant further description; and (d) and (e) are described below.

6.5.2 The Nuclear-magnetic-resonance Meter

This device uses a tracer-velocity method, in which the injected tracer is magnetism, which affects the nuclei of any atoms with a substantial dipole moment (such as hydrogen) in the flowing substance (Figure 6.13). An array of permanent magnets is used to impart the magnetism continuously, and some electromagnetic devices not shown in Figure 6.13 are used to amplify and stabilise it. This magnetising system is followed immediately by an electrical demagnetiser, which is switched on intermittently at regular intervals, thus producing a series of alternate bands of magnetised and demagnetised fluid. The time taken by these bands to travel from the demagnetiser to a detector placed downstream is measured, and from this the mean flow velocity and hence the flowrate are derived.

This is a complex and expensive device with a high performance. Its main field of use is for metering 'difficult' liquids, in situations where good repeatability of measurement is required.

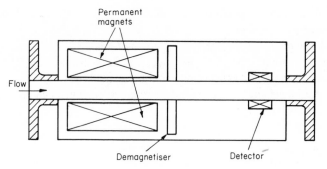

Figure 6.13 *Simplified schematic arrangement of the nuclear-magnetic-resonance flowmeter*

6.5.3 Thermal Flowmeters

These are flowmeters—that is, instruments for determining the total flowrate in a pipe or duct—and must not be confused with hot-resistor or hot-wire anemometers (*see* sections 7.4 and 7.5) which are devices for measuring velocity at a point.

As will appear from *Figure 6.14* they utilise the tracer-dilution principle, with heat acting as the injected tracer. It is obvious that, other things being equal, the temperature rise $(T_2 - T_1)$ will be inversely proportional to the flowrate. Mass flowrate is given by

$$Q_M = \frac{H}{c_p(T_2 - T_1)} \tag{6.3}$$

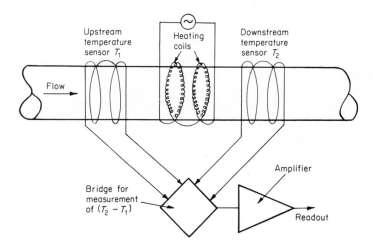

Figure 6.14 *Principle of the thermal (tracer-type) flowmeter*

where H is the power supplied in the form of heat, and c_p is the specific heat capacity at constant pressure.

At present the main use for this type of flowmeter is with gases at relatively low pressures and low flowrates—for instance, in small ventilating ducts and stacks. They cannot be used efficiently where the mass flowrate is high, because there they would consume an uneconomic amount of energy. Their accuracy and initial cost are moderate.

6.6 Flow Indicators

Flow indicators are cheap, simple devices that show at a glance whether fluid is flowing or not. They usually have some sort of transparent section—often in the shape of a dome—containing a solid object which moves when flow occurs. It may be a hinged flap, or a ball which rises, or a spinner which rotates—the possibilities are almost endless.

It is usually a waste of money to install a flowmeter unless you really want to know *how much* flow. If the question is simply, 'flow, or no flow?' a flow indicator will nearly always be a better buy.

6.7 Where to Learn More

Of the instruments discussed in this chapter, the only one to have been on the market long enough to become the subject of a standard is the electromagnetic flowmeter. An English version of a Japanese standard on this subject was published in 1976[1], and at the time of writing the publication of both a British Standard and an ISO Technical Note is pending.

The fundamental theory of the electromagnetic flowmeter has a textbook devoted to it[2]. Of the many papers on this instrument, one of particular interest to users deals with the effect of the upstream pipework on its behaviour[3]. A recent paper by Lock describes an electromagnetic flowmeter with an exceptionally good performance[4].

Useful review papers on ultrasonic flowmeters, with extensive bibliographies, have been written—in the UK by Jespersen[5] and in the USA by McShane[6]. There is a large and rapidly expanding body of literature on vortex-shedding meters, with review papers appearing from time to time, a particularly helpful one being by Medlock[7]. Dijstelbergen[8] has given a user's view of the Swirlmeter, and Adams[9] has described his company's fluidic meter.

The nuclear-magnetic-resonance flowmeter has been described by Genthe[10], thermal flowmeters have been reviewed by Benson[11], and a recent development in gas ionisation meters has been reported by Brain *et al.*[12].

References

1   *Japanese Standard JIS Z 8764-1975.* Method of flow measurement by electromagnetic flowmeters, Association Francaise de Normalisation, Paris (1976)

2   Shercliff, J. A., *The theory of electromagnetic flow measurement,* University Press, Cambridge (1962).

3   Scott, R. W. W., 'A practical assessment of the performance of electro-magnetic flowmeters'. In E. A. Spencer and W. J. Ramsay (Eds.), *Fluid flow measurement in the mid 1970s,* HMSO, Edinburgh, 339-361 (1977)

4   Lock, J. E., 'Electromagnetic flowmeters with ultra stable zero', *Processing,* **22** (April), 53 and 55 (1976)

5   Jespersen, K. I., 'A review of the use of ultrasonics in flow measurement', *NEL Report No. 552,* National Engineering Laboratory, East Kilbride, Glasgow (1973)

6   McShane, J. L., 'Ultrasonic flowmeters'. In R. B. Dowdell (Ed.), *Flow, its Measurement and Control in Science and Industry, Vol. 1, Part 2,* Instrument Society of America, Pittsburgh, 897-915 (1974)

7   Medlock, R. S., 'The vortex flowmeter, its development and characteristics'. Proc. I.I.C.A. Conference, Melbourne, 1975 (Australian Instrument Society)

8   Dijstelbergen, H. H., 'The performance of a swirl flowmeter', *J. Phys. E,* **3,** 886-888 (1970)

9   Adams, R. B., 'A fluidic flowmeter', *Proc. Int. Conf. at Houston, Texas, 15-18 October 1973, Paper 73-815,* Instrument Society of America, Pittsburgh (1973)

10 Genthe, W. K., 'The nuclear-magnetic-resonance flowmeter, process flow measurement experience'. In R. B. Dowdell (Ed.), *Flow, its Measurement and Control in Science and Industry, Vol. 1, Part 2,* Instrument Society of America, Pittsburgh, 849-856 (1974)

11 Benson, J. M., 'Survey of thermal devices for measuring flow.' In R. B. Dow-dell (Ed.), *Flow, its Measurement and Control in Science and Industry, Vol. 1, Part 2,* Instrument Society of America, Pittsburgh, 549-554 (1974)

12 Brain, T. J. S., Reid, J. and MacDonald, C., 'Further developments of the NEL pulsed gas ionization meter', In E. A. Spencer and W. J. Ramsay (Eds.), *Flow, its Measurement and Control in Science and Industry,* Instrument Society of America, Pittsburgh, 317-335 (1974)

7

Fluid Velocity Measuring Instruments and Insertion Meters

The gods . . . . *make instruments to plague us.*

Shakespeare

7.1 Introduction

Thus far this book has been concerned with meters for measuring total flow and flowrate in pipes. We come now to instruments of a related but essentially different type, namely instruments for measuring the velocity at a point of a flowing fluid.

These are used in particular for the following purposes.

(a) To measure wind velocity. (Velocity meters used for this purpose are usually called 'anemometers'.)

(b) To indicate the air speed of aircraft.

(c) To enable an estimate to be made of the velocity of a large body of flowing water, such as a river or an ocean current. (Velocity meters used in this way are often termed 'current meters'.)

(d) To make a measurement of the velocity at one point in a large pipe or duct, from which the approximate flowrate of the gas or liquid can be inferred. (Velocity meters used like this are called 'insertion meters'.)

(e) To measure the velocities at many points over one cross-section of a large pipe or duct, so that the total flowrate can be deduced from these velocities fairly accurately by a process of numerical or graphical integration.

(f) To study velocity distributions in experimental work.

Throughout most of this chapter, velocity meters will be classified according to their construction and principle of operation, rather than by their field of use. At the end, however, insertion meters and integration techniques will be discussed separately.

Cup-type anemometers, which are widely used for meteorological purposes, are not included because they cannot fairly be described as measuring velocity *at a point.*

7.2 Pitot Tubes

7.2.1 How They Work

The oldest and simplest form of fluid velocity meter—and still perhaps the most widely used—is the pitot tube. In its simplest form it is nothing more than a small tube pointing directly upstream, as in *Figure 7.1a.* The fluid in the mouth of the tube has been brought to rest, and its kinetic energy has been converted to pressure energy, which creates an enhanced pressure inside the pitot tube. It follows from Bernoulli's equation that δP, the excess of pressure inside the pitot tube over the static pressure outside it, will be in the ideal case

$$\delta P = \tfrac{1}{2}\rho v^2 \tag{7.1}$$

and in a practical situation

$$\delta P = C \times \tfrac{1}{2}\rho v^2 \tag{7.2}$$

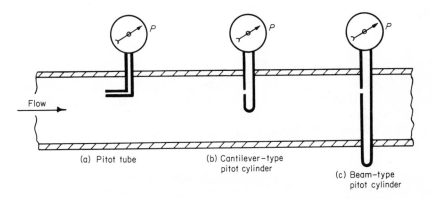

Figure 7.1 *Three types of total-head pitot device (shown diagrammatically)*

where C is a calibration coefficient which, for a well designed pitot tube, should be very close to unity—perhaps even within ±0.2% of unity.

An alternative form of pitot tube is the pitot cylinder, shown in *Figures 7.1b* and *c.* This is a tube with a closed end and a hole in its wall; it is rather more robust and handier to insert in a pipe than the ordinary pitot tube, but not quite so accurate.

The pressure indicated by a gauge connected directly to a pitot tube or cylinder is the *total* pressure. To obtain the required *differential* pressure, δP, it is necessary to take away the static pressure in the vicinity. The required subtraction is invariably done directly, by using a manometer or differential pressure gauge, with the pitot connected to one side and a static pressure tapping connected to the other.

When a pitot cylinder is used in a pipe the static tappings are sited in the pipe wall, in the vicinity of the pitot. Static tappings in the pipe wall are also used occasionally in conjunction with pitot tubes. However, it is often more convenient to employ a pitot-static tube *(Figure 7.2)*. This consists of two concentric tubes, the inner one acting as a pitot tube and the outer as a means of measuring static pressure. Pitot-static tubes are essential in rough-walled pipes or where swirl is present, because in such circumstances static tappings in the pipe wall give faulty readings.

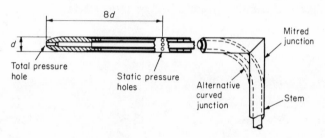

Figure 7.2 *One type of pitot-static tube*

Pitot-type probes with two or more openings facing in different directions are sometimes used where information about the direction of the flow as well as its speed is required.

Another variation on the pitot tube which was once very popular is the pitot-

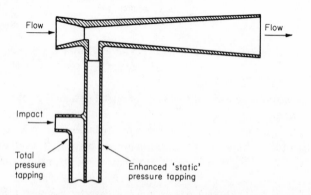

Figure 7.3 *The simplest form of pitot–venturi probe*

venturi. This appeared in several forms, one of which is shown in *Figure 7.3*. By taking the low pressure from a tapping in the venturi throat instead of at a static tapping, an enhanced pressure differential is obtained. It was realised rather belatedly that this benefit was largely negated by errors from other sources, and the pitot-venturi is no longer held in its former esteem.

7.2.2 Advantages

(a) The pitot probe is a simple, inexpensive and durable instrument.
(b) In skilled hands it can give extremely accurate results, and even an inexperienced operator can obtain moderate accuracy from it.
(c) With the aid of a suitable switching device it is possible for one differential-pressure measuring system to serve a large number of adjacent pitot tubes.
(d) Although its normal use is to measure air velocity, it can be used with practically any fluid.

7.2.3 Disadvantages

(a) Its main disadvantage is one that it shares with differential-pressure flow-meters—a square root characteristic. This not only complicates the processing of its readings, but also means that the rangeability is limited. To obtain meaningful values of δP at low air velocities it is necessary to use a very sensitive and delicate micromanometer (*see* section 12.1).
(b) Its accuracy can be impaired by the presence of swirl, especially if pipe-wall static tappings are used.
(c) If flow pulsations are present, special care is needed if serious errors are to be avoided (*see* section 8.2).
(d) The combination of pitot tube, static tapping, differential pressure indicator, and the tubes connecting them together makes up a rather unwieldy system which takes time to set up; it is therefore not well suited to quick 'one-off' measurements.
(e) At very high air velocities it is influenced by 'Mach number effects' as the velocity of sound is approached, and at very low velocities by viscous effects, but the former extreme is rarely encountered outside the aircraft industry and the latter hardly ever occurs in ordinary engineering applications.

7.2.4 When to Use Them

The main use of pitot tubes is in the measurement of air flow in wind tunnels, test rigs and ventilating ducts. They are used both to study the velocity distribution over a large area, and in conjunction with an integration technique (*see* section 7.9) to indicate the total flow in large ducts.

The technique of using pitot tubes under any circumstances, but especially inside ducts and tunnels, is an art where practice makes perfect. Putting a single pitot tube in a ventilation duct to give a rough indication of the flowrate is well within any engineer's capability; but traversing all over a cross-section to obtain data for integration, to give flowrate to within ±1%, is a job for a thoroughly experienced operator.

7.3 Propeller-type Current Meters and Vane-type Anemometers

7.3.1 How They Work

These devices are the velocity meter equivalent of the turbine flowmeter. They consist of a small free-spinning rotor through which the flow passes axially, and an electrical or mechanical system for counting the total number of revolutions.

Figure 7.4 *An array of current meters in a large pipe (photo: NEL)*

Although those types with an electrical readout—which means virtually all propeller-type current meters and many vane anemometers—could be used to give an instantaneous value of flowrate, this is rarely done. It is usual to count the total number of revolutions during a measured period of time, and hence to evaluate the mean flowrate over that period.

The propeller-type current meter is for liquid flows. It is sometimes used on its own, but is more commonly used in batteries spread over the cross-section of a river or a very large pipe, as shown in *Figure 7.4,* for the purpose of total flow-rate integration (*see* section 7.9).

Vane anemometers, illustrated in *Figure 7.5,* are shaped like miniature wind-mills. They are quite often used singly at a fixed location, but may also be used for traversing or in batteries where total flowrate is required.

Figure 7.5 *Some typical vane anemometers (photo: NEL)*

7.3.2 Advantages

(a) Wide rangeability—much more than 10 to 1.
(b) Practically linear output.
(c) Little affected by variations in fluid density (except at very low velocities).
(d) Easy to use.
(e) Inexpensive.

7.3.3 Disadvantages

(a) Because the bearing can be damaged by careless handling and may be affected by dirt particles, they may need periodical recalibration if high accuracy is to be obtained over a long period.

(b) They are very sensitive to swirl.

(c) Because of their relatively large size they cannot be regarded as giving a true 'point velocity', except in very large flow passages—and even there they cannot be used to measure velocity very close to the wall.

(d) The blades of vane anemometers are easily bent, and if this happens recalibration is always necessary.

7.4 Hot-Resistor Anemometers

7.4.1 How They Work

The basic principle is very simple: an electrically heated element is placed within the stream of air or gas, and the higher the velocity the more it tends to cool the element; the change in temperature causes a change in resistance, which can be measured by some appropriate circuitry. A great many variations upon this simple theme are possible, and nowadays there is a large and bewildering variety of hot-resistor instruments on the market.

First of all, there are two ways of seeing how much the wind is cooling the element. It is possible to keep a constant current flowing and see how much the resistance (and hence the temperature) has changed; or one can use a feedback system to keep the resistance (and temperature) constant and see how much the applied voltage has changed. The constant-current system is simpler and cheaper, but the constant-temperature system responds better to rapid changes in air velocity.

Then there are the variations in the nature of the resistor. This may be a wire or filament, which may be of platinum, or platinum-coated tungsten, or some other metal or combination of metals; and the wire may be either bare or enclosed in a protective sheath; or the resistor may be a thin film of conductive metal deposited on a non-conductive support; or it may be a thermistor.

Each type of resistor has its particular uses. The bare wire element has much the fastest response, and is therefore suited to measuring pulsating flow, but because of its small diameter, dust contamination seriously alters its surface area and hence its rate of cooling. Also, the fine wire is fragile, so that this type is easily damaged both by careless handling and by excessive air speeds, which means that its rangeability is somewhat limited. The sheathed wire element and the film element, on the other hand, are more robust, less sensitive to contamination, are easily cleaned, and can be used over a wider range; but their slower response leads to incorrect readings when the flow is rapidly changing or pulsating. Thermistors have a much greater change of resistance with temperature than metal wires or films, and are therefore useful for measuring very low velocities, but their performance in most other respects is inferior.

Finally, there are two basically different ways of using hot-resistor probes. The calibration curve (output versus velocity) of the basic instrument is not linear, although it is nothing like the square root calibration curve of the pitot tube; in addition, the calibration is to some extent dependent upon the actual temperature of the element, as well as upon the density and the thermal properties of the gas. In highly accurate work it is necessary for the operator to take the output of the basic instrument and apply various corrections to it. Where convenience is more important an instrument will have linearising and temperature-compensating circuits built in, so that it reads directly in metres per second when used with air at pressures near ambient, but these direct-reading instruments are not very accurate. For example, one of the most popular instruments of this kind claims an accuracy of only ±2% *of full scale* (*see* section 2.3.3).

Some special designs are also available for special purposes. These include multi-element probes for measuring velocity vectors in 2 or 3 dimensions, and cooled elements for work in hot gases.

Numerous attempts have been made to apply the hot-resistor principle to the measurement of velocities in liquids, but the practical problems are severe and commercial hot-resistor liquid velocimeters have not yet gained widespread acceptance.

Figure 7.6 *A small hot-wire probe (photo: DISA)*

7.4.2 Advantages and Disadvantages

It will be apparent from the previous section that hot-resistor anemometers constitute a large family, so that different members have different advantages and disadvantages. The user has to decide which particular properties are important to him. In particular he has to ask himself: do I want . . .

convenience of operation—or high accuracy?

very fast response—or robustness and very wide rangeability?

. . . because one cannot have it both ways.

One advantage that all members of the family share is compactness, which is instanced by the photograph of a typical small hot-wire probe in *Figure 7.6*. Disadvantages include the need for periodical recalibration if high accuracy is to be maintained and a liability to radiation errors when used near solid surfaces.

7.4.3 Points to Watch when Buying and Using

Because there are so many different types on the market, great care is necessary at the purchasing stage or you will end up with something less than ideal for your purpose. Send the manufacturers a precise statement of what the velocimeter has to do, and ask them to quote for the cheapest device on their list which will do the job adequately; and, having bought it, do not subsequently put the instrument to work on a job with an entirely different specification!

To some extent this difficulty can be overcome by buying a multi-purpose kit, consisting of one 'black box' with two or more probes of different types. Whatever you buy it is as well to remember that probes have a limited life, especially those of the unshielded hot-wire type. By carrying several spare probes a lot of delay and frustration may be avoided.

7.5 Another Type of Hot-wire Anemometer

There is another type of hot-wire anemometer which is quite different from the hot-resistor types described above, although it is sometimes confused with them. The best known representative of this type is perhaps the Simmons hot-wire anemometer.

In instruments of this kind the hot wire is purely a heating element, and in contrast with the hot-resistor instruments it is made of a material with a low temperature coefficient of resistivity. Temperature change is sensed by an adjacent thermocouple, which is so positioned that the voltage generated by it is roughly proportional to the product of density and velocity for any one gas. Because of this it can under favourable circumstances be made to function as a true mass flowmeter (*see* section 8.1).

Both shielded and unshielded versions of this type of anemometer are available commercially. Some enthusiastic users consider that it has important advantages over the hot-resistor type and deserves to be more widely known than it is.

7.6 Some Other Non-mechanical Fluid Velocity Meters

7.6.1 Introduction

Practically every physical principle that can be used as the basis of a flowmeter can also be used, with appropriate modifications, to make a velocity meter—and most of them have been. In this section we shall briefly consider five veloci-meters of widely different types which have reached the market and appear to be serving a useful purpose.

7.6.2 Electromagnetic Velocity Meters

Like its flowmeter counterpart, this type of velocity meter will work only with water and water-based liquids. It is rather like a miniature electromagnetic flow-meter turned inside out, with field coils inside a small probe causing a voltage to be generated when water passes by the outside of the probe.

Provided that it is calibrated and the electrodes are kept clean, it should measure velocity with an accuracy of ±2 or 3% over a velocity range of 5 to 1— but in practice users often find it difficult to achieve this level, especially when working in the sea. Although other types of velocity meter can beat this per-formance, the electromagnetic type can probably claim to be more trouble-free when used in dirty liquids, since there are no mechanical parts to wear or tappings to block up, and it is designed for easy cleaning of the electrodes.

Models for use in open water and models for use in pipes are available.

7.6.3 Ultrasonic Velocity Meters

For practical reasons it is difficult to make a neat, compact ultrasonic device which will measure ultrasonic velocity accurately at the point where it is inserted. A so-called ultrasonic current meter has been produced but it is a bulky, expensive, high-performance device. It is primarily of use in the open sea, where local velocities vary very little, so that one large meter capable of measuring accurately the velocity in one place is more useful than a large number of small meters of moderate accuracy spread over a large area. It works on much the same principle as the single-path diagonal-beam meter (*see* section 6.2.2) except that in this case there are two paths at right angles on the same frame, so that velocity vectors in two dimensions can be measured.

Doppler-effect ultrasonic velocity meters are also used for ocean work in situations where lower accuracies are acceptable.

7.6.4 The Jet-deflection Fluidic Velocity Meter

This device has practically nothing in common with the fluidic flowmeter
described in section 6.4.1, since it depends upon an entirely different fluidics
technique.

It is intended solely for measuring air or gas velocity, and its principle of
operation is illustrated in *Figure 7.7*. Air or gas is supplied to a fine nozzle from

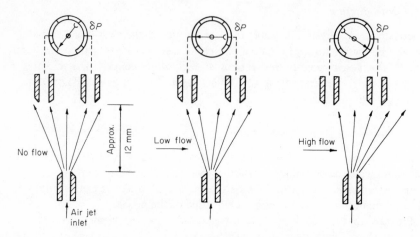

Figure 7.7 *Principle of the jet-deflection fluidic velocity meter*

which it issues at a little less than sonic velocity. The issuing jet travels for about
12 mm at right angles to the stream whose velocity is to be measured, and then
strikes a pair of receiver-nozzles connected to a differential pressure gauge.

When the main stream velocity is zero, the jet falls equally upon the two
receiver-nozzles and δP is zero. As the stream velocity increases the jet falls more
and more asymmetrically upon the receiver-nozzles, and δP increases in direct
proportion to the stream velocity.

The result is a simple velocity meter without either moving parts or electrical
connections, whose readout, like that of the pitot tube, is a differential pressure.
Unlike the pitot tube, however, it has a linear output, a very wide rangeability,
a worthwhile readout at extremely low velocities, and a very fast response to
fluctuating flow.

Against that impressive list of advantages must be set the following disadvantages. Its claimed accuracy (±2% of full scale) is much less than that of a pitot
tube at high velocities; it requires a supply of compressed air or gas; and slight
damage or fouling in one of the nozzles can affect its calibration. Also, its output
is proportional to the square root of gas density and corrections for density
variation are rather inconvenient to make.

7.6.5 The 'Ionflo' Ion-deflection Velocity Meter

This air velocity meter is curiously reminiscent of the jet-deflection meter of
section 7.6.4. The probe consists of a short length of tube, in the centre of which
a disc energised by a high electric potential is supported *(Figure 7.8)*. This emits
a stream of ions which strike the interior wall of the probe in a region that is
coated with a resistive material.

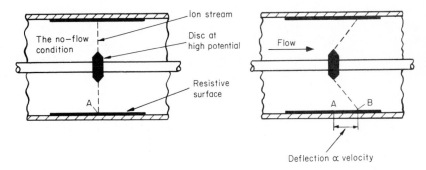

Figure 7.8 *Principle of the ion-deflection velocity meter*

When there is no flow through the probe the ions strike the resistive surface
at A. When flow occurs the ion stream is deflected downstream, and strikes the
surface at B. The distance AB is directly proportional to the velocity in the probe,
and the analysing circuitry converts the signal directly into a digital indication of
velocity.

Like the jet-deflection meter it is only of moderate accuracy (±2% of full
scale), but has a very wide rangeability and can be used to measure extremely
low velocities. It is superior to the jet-deflection meter in its ability to tolerate
a dusty environment, and in having an output directly proportional to gas
density (and hence to mass flowrate), but inferior to it in being affected disast-
rously by high levels of humidity in the gas.

7.6.6 Vortex-shedding Velocity Meters

Velocity meters based on the same principle as the vortex-shedding flowmeter
(*see* section 6.3) are available. They are probably the only velocity meters with
the following combination of advantages: digital output; linear characteristic;
wide rangeability; and freedom from moving parts. Their biggest disadvantage is
that they obstruct the flow they are supposed to measure, and cannot indicate
a true point velocity.

7.7 Laser–Doppler Velocity Meters

The laser–Doppler velocimeter has been left to the last because it is in a class of its own. Unlike all the velocity meters described so far it is not suitable for routine use in an industrial or an outdoor environment, but is rather a tool for the research and development laboratory—albeit an extremely valuable one.

7.7.1 How They Work

A simplified schematic arrangement of a laser–Doppler velocimeter is given in *Figure 7.9*. The laser beam is first passed into a beam-splitting prism, and then the two parallel component beams are passed through a lens which makes them converge at a point where the flow velocity is to be measured. In an ideal world this 'point' would be only a few wavelengths wide; in practice, the region

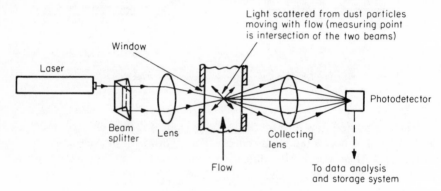

Figure 7.9 *Principle of the laser–Doppler velocity meter*

occupied by the intersecting beams is something like 0.1 mm across.

Whenever a dirt particle passes through the bright spot where the two beams intersect, it reflects light in all directions. This reflected light possesses a Doppler frequency shift. Some of it is picked up by a collecting lens and focussed upon a photodetector, whose output when suitably processed gives a value of the fluid velocity at the point where the beams intersect. With some additional refinements the system can be used to measure velocity vectors in two or three dimensions.

7.7.2 Advantages

(a) It is the only high-performance fluid velocimeter that does not in any way obstruct the flow.

(b) It comes very close to the ideal of measuring velocity at a precisely defined point—much closer, in fact, than any other fluid velocimeter.

(c) Because it is such a fine tool it can be used closer to a solid boundary than any other instrument, and can be used to study small-scale turbulence.

(d) Its readings are absolute indications of velocity—in other words, it does not need calibration.

(e) It has high accuracy over a wide range of velocity, and can be used down to a few mm s^{-1}.

(f) It can be used with both gases and liquids. (The common term 'laser–Doppler *anemometer*' is misleading, in view of this.)

(g) Its readout is independent of all fluid properties except refractive index.

7.7.3 Disadvantages

(a) The working fluid must be reasonably transparent, and if the fluid is contained in a pipe or duct this must have windows.

(b) Very clean fluids may need to be seeded with a small amount of fine dust.

(c) The instrument is expensive, fragile and complex, and it needs a skilled operator.

7.8 Insertion Meters

7.8.1 The Three-quarter-radius Meter

Most of the velocity-measuring instruments described above have a small measuring head which could, if necessary, be inserted through a small opening in the wall of a pipe or duct. (The two exceptions are the ultrasonic current meter, and the laser–Doppler velocimeter.) Some of the flowmeters mentioned in earlier chapters, including the drag-plate meter (section 4.1) have also been modified so that they can be used as velocity meters. When a fluid velocity meter is designed to be inserted through a flanged opening in a pipe or duct, and sealed in place so that it can be left there more or less permanently to give an approximate indication of the flowrate, it is termed an insertion meter.

If the pipe or duct is circular it is usual for the insertion meter to be installed at a distance $0.75R$ from the centre, where R is the radius. This is because experience has shown that the velocity at this position is approximately equal to the mean pipe velocity, *provided that the flow profile is fully developed* (*see* section 1.2.3). This is a very important proviso. If the insertion meter is sited too close to a bend, errors of 10% or more can easily result. And it should be remembered that, even with a perfect flow profile, the ratio of the three-quarter-radius velocity to the mean velocity is not exactly unity; indeed, it varies with Reynolds number and pipe wall roughness, over a range which can easily be from 0.98 to 1.02.

The three-quarter-radius insertion meter must therefore be regarded as a device of very moderate accuracy. The accuracy can, of course, be increased considerably if the meter can be calibrated *in situ*. If this is done, remember that it will probably need recalibrating *in situ* whenever it is taken out for cleaning and maintenance and then replaced.

A substantial improvement in accuracy can be made by inserting four three-quarter-radius meters on one cross-section, spaced at 90° intervals, and averaging their readings. However, this has never proved a popular solution because of its cost.

7.8.2 The 'Annubar'

The Annubar is a proprietary insertion meter based on the pitot principle *(Figure 7.10)*. The tube, A, is a pitot cylinder extending right across the pipe, and containing four carefully spaced holes facing upstream. The tube B is sited inside A, and is connected to it only through an opening level with the centre of A. In this way the pressure in B is some kind of average of the total pressures at the four holes in A—although not a theoretically justifiable average.

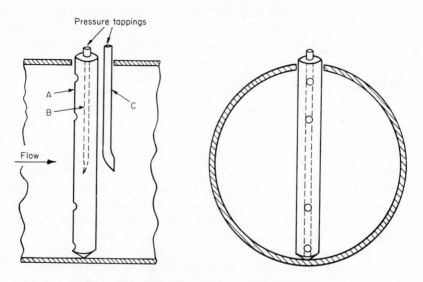

Figure 7.10 *The 'Annubar' insertion meter*

The tube C has an opening facing downstream on the pipe centre line, so that it registers a pressure rather less than the static pressure on account of the suction effect. Because of this the readout of the Annubar, which consists of the pressure differential between tubes B and C, is rather greater than that of a conventional pitot cylinder with wall tappings.

Experience has shown that the Annubar is less sensitive to upstream flow disturbances than a three-quarter-radius insertion meter. You should never site *any* insertion meter close to an upstream bend or valve if you can avoid it—but if you cannot possibly avoid it, then the Annubar insertion meter affords a way of making the best out of a bad job.

7.9 Velocity–Area Integration Techniques

These techniques are widely used for the accurate measurement of flowrate in very large pipes or ducts, where the flows are too great for direct methods of flow measurement to be used.

7.9.1 The Mathematical Principles

If an array of meters is used to measure the velocity at a large number of points on one cross-section of a pipe or duct, the flowrate can then be derived from an integration over the total area of cross-section. This integration takes account of the fact that much more fluid is flowing in a one-centimetre-wide annulus near the pipe wall than in a one-centimetre annulus near the centre. Old-timers can still remember the days when the integration was always carried out graphically, but nowadays numerical methods have largely taken over because they are generally more convenient. These integration techniques fall into two categories.

First, there are methods which involve making the measurements at mathematically predetermined positions, such that a simple arithmetic mean of the results then leads directly to the mean pipe velocity. Two ways of positioning the velocimeters to attain this end are in common use: the log-linear method[1] for circular cross-sections, and the log-Tchebychev method[2,3] for both circular and rectangular cross-sections. The log-Tchebychev positions for a rectangular cross-section and 6 × 5 points are shown in *Figure 7.11;* the positions for many other cases are tabulated in the references cited. These methods simplify enormously the job of calculating the results, but they leave the operator no choice as to where he puts his probes. Sometimes they cannot be used because of the physical impossibility of getting the outermost probes close enough to the wall.

The alternative method is for the operator to site the probes where he can, and then to use an appropriate numerical technique to evaluate the integral. The 'method of cubics'[2-4] is normally used for this procedure; in experienced hands it gives very accurate results but involves some exceedingly complicated arithmetic, which is hardly practicable without the use of a computer.

With either method, the accuracy of the final result depends upon the number of points at which measurements are made. Ideally, there should be about 36 points—in a circular cross-section that means six on each of 6 equi-spaced radii. (It is rarely cost-effective to exceed this number.) There should never be less than

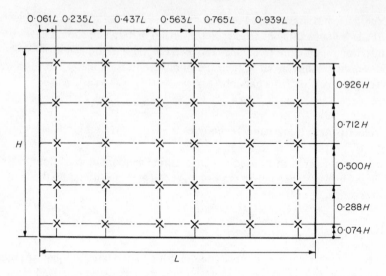

Figure 7.11 *Log-Tchebychev positions for 6 × 5 points in a rectangular duct*

12 points—three on each of 4 equi-spaced radii, if the cross-section is circular. Also, the number of radii should never be less than the number of points on each radius.

Whatever method is used it is essential for the probes to be positioned accurately.

7.9.2 The Experimental Techniques

The velocity–area integration method is not a job for dabblers. It is impossible here to give more than a brief outline of the experimental techniques involved. Anyone proposing to use the method will find it absolutely essential to begin by studying one or more of the relevant standard specifications[2,3,5,6].

Once again there is a choice between two fundamentally different approaches. It is possible to set up an array of measuring heads, one at every measuring station, as shown in *Figure 7.4*, in which case all the measurements are made simultaneously. This method is costly in equipment but economical of experimental time; it is the usual method in very large pipes and ducts.

In medium-sized pipes and ducts an alternative method known as 'traversing' is usually employed. A measuring head—some form of pitot probe is most commonly used for this purpose—is pushed further and further into the pipe, so that successive readings are taken at different positions on one diameter or one line of a rectangular grid. Then it is removed and inserted on another diameter or grid line, and the process is repeated. This method consumes more time in actual measurement, but requires much less equipment and involves less setting-up time. Another form of traversing is often carried out in tunnels and mines, where the operator is actually inside the flow passage; the accuracy in this method depends largely upon the operator's skill in avoiding blockage errors caused by the positioning of his own body or his hand.

Because the individual readings during a series of traverses are spaced over a long period of time, the flowrate is likely to fluctuate during the test. This must be allowed for by a process known as 'normalising'. A single probe is inserted on another cross-section at a fixed position and is used as a reference. Its reading, v_1, is noted at the same time as each individual reading, v_x, during the traverse, and the values of v_1 are used to determine what each value of v_x would have been if the flowrate in the duct (and hence v_1) had remained constant throughout the traversing.

If the whole operation is carried out with great care, the resulting value of flowrate should be accurate to within about ±1%.

7.10 Where to Learn More

There is a great deal of published information on pitot tubes. Of particular value are two of the standards mentioned above[3,5], a substantial book emanating from NPL[7], and two important papers[8,9].

A number of standard specifications on current meters have already been published and others are pending. The most important international standards are listed in the bibliography[2,10,11]; corresponding national standards have been or are about to be published in several countries. There is a useful section on vane anemometers with a good bibliography in a book by Roberts[12], and a rather older publication by Swirles and Hinsley[13] is also valuable.

A large amount of literature has been published on hot-resistor anemometers, but as yet no international standard specifications. The best general introduction to the subject is probably a survey paper published (gratis) by a manufacturer[14]; it contains a bibliography of 142 references. The Simmons-type hot-wire anemometer has been described by Cowdrey[15].

For information on various ultrasonic velocimeters *see* the paper by Hardies[16]. A useful survey paper on laser-Doppler meters with an extensive bibliography[17] has been issued on the same basis as Reference 14. A comparative study of various velocity–area integration techniques has recently been published by Kinghorn and McHugh[18], and the classic paper by Preston on the three-quarter-radius pitot tube[19] is still of interest despite its age. There are several international standards on velocity–area integration techniques[2,3,20] and the American Society for Testing and Materials has published two standards on gas velocity measurement in ducts using pitot tubes[21] and thermal anemometers[22].

References

1 Winternitz, F. A. L. and Fischl, C. F., 'A simplified integration technique for pipe flow measurement', *Water Power*, **9**, 225–234 (1957)

2 *ISO Standard 3354 (1975)*. Measurement of clean water flow in closed conduits—velocity area method using current meters

3 *ISO Standard 3966 (1976)*. Measurement of clean water flow in closed conduits—velocity area method using pitot-static tubes

4 Kinghorn, F. C., McHugh, A. and Duncan, W., 'An experimental comparison of two velocity–area numerical integration techniques', *Water Power*, **25**, 330–335 (1973)

5 *British Standard 1042 (1973)*. Methods for the measurement of fluid flow in pipes. Part 2A: Pitot tubes, Class A accuracy.

6 *AMCA Standard 210–74* and *ASHRAE Standard 51–75*. Laboratory methods of testing fans for rating purposes. Air Moving and Conditioning Association, Inc., Arlington Heights (Illinois) and American Society of Heating, Refrigerating and Air-conditioning Engineers, New York (1975)

7 Bryer, D. W. and Pankhurst, R. C., *Pressure probe methods for determining wind speed and flow direction*, HMSO, London (1971)

8 Preston, J. H. and Norbury, J. F., 'The three-quarter-radius flowmeter', Paper A-5 in Proceedings of NEL Symposium, *Flow Measurement in Closed Conduits*, HMSO, Edinburgh (1962)

9 Winternitz, F. A. L., 'Cantilevered pitot cylinder', *Engineer, Lond.*, **199**, 729–732 (1955)

10 *ISO Standard 2537 (1974)*. Liquid flow measurement in open channels— cup-type and propellor-type current meters

11 *ISO Standard 3455 (1976)*. Liquid flow measurement in open channels— calibration of rotating-element current meters in straight open tanks

12 Roberts, A., *Mine ventilation*, Cleaver-Hume Press, London (1960)

13 Swirles, J. and Hinsley, F. B., 'The use of vane anemometers in the measurement of air flow', *Trans. Inst. Mining Eng.*, **113**, 896–923 (1954)

14 Anon., *Anemometer systems*, Section III: Theory and Applications, Thermo Systems Inc., St. Paul, Minnesota (1975)

15 Cowdrey, C. F., 'Temperature and pressure corrections to be applied to the shielded hot-wire anemometer', *Brit. J. Appl. Phys.*, **9**, 112–116 (1958)

16 Hardies, C. E., 'An advanced two-axis acoustic current meter', Paper 2293, Proc. 1975 Offshore Technology Conf., Houston, **2**, 465–476

17 Anon., *Laser anemometer systems*, Appendix, Technical Data and Bibliography, Thermo Systems Inc., St. Paul, Minnesota (no date)

18 Kinghorn, F. C. and McHugh, A., 'An international comparison of integration techniques for traverse methods in flow measurement', *La Houille Blanche*, **1977** No. 1, 49–58

19 Preston, J. H., 'The three-quarter-radius pitot tube flowmeter', *Engineer, Lond.*, **190**, 400–402 (1950)

20 *ISO Standard 748 (1973).* Liquid flow measurement in open channels by velocity area methods (revised edition due for publication shortly)
21 *ASTM Standard D 3154-72.* Test for average velocity in a duct (pitot tube method)
22 *ASTM Standard D 3195-73.* Test for average velocity in a duct using a thermal anemometer

8

Special Problems in Flow Metering

The job was a job that just couldn't be done,
But it had to be done, and he knew it.
So he tackled that job that just couldn't be done
—And found that he couldn't do it!

Author unknown

8.1 Mass Flow Measurement

There are two alternative ways to tackle the problem of measuring mass flowrate. One is to design a meter whose response is a function of mass flowrate only, so that a knowledge of the physical properties of the fluid is not necessary. Such meters are known as 'true mass flowmeters'.

The other approach is to make simultaneous measurements of both the volumetric flowrate and the fluid's density (or, if its composition is constant and its *PVT* properties are known, its pressure and temperature, from which its density can be derived), and then to compute the mass flowrate. A system which does this is known as an 'inferential mass flow measurement system'.

Many different mass flow measurement methods have been tried in the laboratory, and quite a number have been used in industry. Those discussed below are believed to include most if not all the methods of industrial importance today.

8.1.1 Angular-momentum Meters

The angular-momentum meter is a popular kind of true mass flowmeter. The principle of one type is illustrated in *Figure 8.1*. An impeller is rotated by an external motor at a constant speed, and the whole of the flowing fluid passes between the longitudinal vanes of this impeller. The fluid is thereby made to rotate at a constant angular velocity, and consequently the angular momentum of the fluid leaving the impeller per second is directly proportional to its mass flowrate.

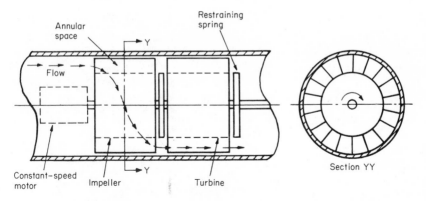

Figure 8.1 *Principle of one type of angular-momentum mass flowmeter*

The rotating fluid then enters the turbine. This is identical with the impeller except that it is not driven, and that it is constrained from rotating very far by a spring. Because all the angular momentum of the fluid is destroyed by the turbine, the torque upon it is equal to the rate of destruction of angular momentum in the turbine, which in turn is equal to the rate of generation of angular momentum in the impeller, and hence is proportional to the mass flowrate. The torque can be inferred from the angular displacement of the turbine against the restraining spring, and so this displacement is a linear function of mass flowrate.

That rather complicated chain of events can be summed up like this:

(a) the impeller generates angular momentum at a rate proportional to mass flowrate;

(b) the turbine destroys it at the same rate—

(c) —which, from Newton's laws of motion, is equal to the torque upon it—

(d) —which, from Hooke's law, is proportional to the angular deflection of the spring restraining the turbine;

(e) therefore the spring deflection is proportional to the mass flowrate.

A disadvantage of this meter is the need for an externally powered motor to drive the impeller at constant speed. This is overcome in another type of angular-momentum meter, in which the impeller is driven by a turbine drawing the necessary power from the flowing fluid.

8.1.2 The 'Wheatstone Bridge' Meter

In this kind of true mass flowmeter, four identical orifices, an independently driven positive displacement pump, and a differential pressure gauge, are all connected with pipework to form a hydraulic analogy of a Wheatstone bridge *(Figure 8.2)*. The two different positions of the pressure gauge, shown in (a) and (b) of *Figure 8.2,* are necessary according to whether the flow to be measured is greater or less than the flow through the pump.

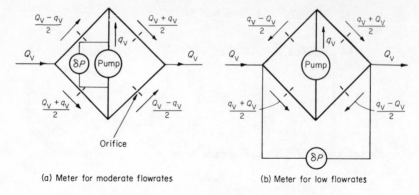

(a) Meter for moderate flowrates   (b) Meter for low flowrates

Figure 8.2 *Principle of the 'Wheatstone bridge' mass flowmeter*

By a mathematical analysis of the flows in the various branches of the network it can be shown that the measured pressure drop, δP, should be directly proportional to the mass flowrate, $Q_V \rho$, which is to be measured. This relationship is not affected by the density, viscosity, or any other property of the fluid; the only proviso is that the density must be the same in every branch of the network—a condition which renders this type of meter unsuitable for use with gases.

Experiments have shown that this theoretical relationship is borne out in practice. The outcome is a family of commercial liquid meters for which remarkable claims are made: an accuracy approaching ±0.5% of the measured value of mass flowrate over a very wide range.

8.1.3 The Thermal Mass Flowmeter

Just as some of Orwell's animals were more equal than others, it would seem that some true mass flowmeters are more true than others! There can be no disputing that the types described above, which are based solely upon fluid-mechanical principles, deserve to be called true mass flowmeters: they can be fed with practically any fluid, without even knowing what it is, and they will indicate the mass flowrate with reasonable accuracy.

Thermal mass flowmeters are often referred to as true mass flowmeters, but the appropriateness of this description in their case is somewhat questionable. Their output depends upon the heat-transfer properties of the fluid, so that if, for instance, they are calibrated with natural gas having a certain composition, and subsequently the gas composition changes, they will give inaccurate readings. On the other hand, because the heat-transfer properties of a gas do not change very rapidly with changes in its density, they can be used with a given gas over a moderate range of temperature and pressure without too much loss of accuracy; this is why enthusiasts refer to them as true mass flowmeters. In general, their performance suffers more from temperature changes than pressure changes, and by keeping the gas temperature fairly closely controlled it is possible to obtain an accuracy approaching ±1% over a wide range of flowrates.

The way this type of meter works was described in section 6.5.3.

8.1.4 Inferential Methods of Measuring Mass Flow

Two basically different systems for measuring mass flow inferentially are in use. They both use a conventional flowmeter to determine volumetric flowrate and/or total volume passed, but two different methods of density determination are involved.

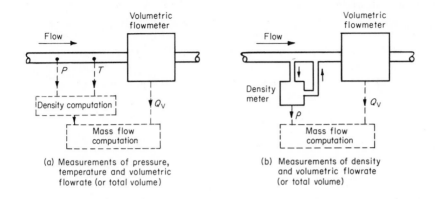

(a) Measurements of pressure, temperature and volumetric flowrate (or total volume)

(b) Measurements of density and volumetric flowrate (or total volume)

Figure 8.3 *Two inferential systems of mass flow measurement*

The system shown in *Figure 8.3a* depends upon a prior knowledge of the *PVT* properties of the fluid being metered—that is to say, the way in which the fluid's specific volume varies with pressure and temperature. Pressure and temperature are both measured upstream of the flowmeter, and density is computed from these measurements. Then a second computation combines the density and the flowmeter reading to give mass flow.

In the other system of *Figure 8.3b,* some of the fluid is passed through a density meter (*see* section 12.3.2) before it enters the flowmeter. Thus density is determined directly, and then its value is combined with the flowmeter output as in the first system. When using this method, take care to ensure that (a) the temperature and pressure of the fluid in the densitometer are the same as in the flowmeter (a slight pressure difference can be tolerated if a correction is applied for it), and (b) that the fluid discharged from the densitometer does not create unacceptable inlet conditions at the flowmeter. Neglect of these precautions is a frequent cause of inaccuracy in systems of this kind.

8.1.5 Which Method for Which Job?

Although there are always exceptions to any set of generalisations, the following
guidelines hold for the great majority of mass flow measurement situations.

(a) True mass flowmeters are best for low flowrates, but inferential systems
for medium and high flowrates.

(b) The Wheatstone bridge meter is for use only with liquids, and its main
field of use is for metering chemicals.

(c) Angular-momentum meters are most often used with liquids, and
especially for metering fuel on aircraft, but they can also be used with gases.

(d) Thermal meters are primarily for use with gases, but can also be used with
liquids. They are rather inaccurate in situations where either the composition
or the temperature of the fluid varies widely. An important advantage is that
they create zero effective head loss; a disadvantage is that they require a
considerable input of energy in all but the smallest sizes.

(e) Of the two inferential systems, the one based on direct measurements of
density is gaining in popularity at the expense of the system based on measurement of P and T; it is undoubtedly the better system in situations where the
composition of the fluid being metered is liable to vary.

8.2 The Measurement of Pulsating Flow

8.2.1 Introduction

The problem of measuring pulsating flow came into prominence in the early part
of this century. Pumps, compressors, steam engines and gas engines of the reciprocating type produce severe pulsations in the flow lines leading to or from them,
and it was found that differential pressure meters—which were the only large
flowrate meters then in general use—gave erroneous readings under such
conditions.

Nowadays reciprocating machinery has largely given way to turbomachinery,
and pulsation troubles are less widespread and usually less severe when they do
arise. Nevertheless, they are still with us in some measure, especially in systems
where large centrifugal fans are used to supply air at high velocity, and it is
therefore important that the effects of pulsation on flowmeters should be clearly
understood.

8.2.2 Types of Error Caused by Pulsating Flow

The effect of even a simple sinusoidal pulsation on a flowmeter is complex, and
that of random or irregular fluctuations in flow is even more complicated. They
cause a number of different forms of error, and most types of flowmeter are
subject to at least two of them. The principal kinds of error arising from flow
pulsations will now be discussed.

(a) *The square root error.* This form of error is peculiar to those types of meter, such as differential pressure devices, pitot tubes and drag-plate meters, which have a square root characteristic. It arises in the following way. If the differential pressure gauge cannot respond as fast as the fluid is pulsating, it will settle down to a steady value which will be roughly the mean of the differential pressures throughout the cycle—and even if the gauge does respond to the pulsations, the operator will only be able to read the mean value. But the square root of this mean value will *not* lead to a correct value of the mean flowrate since the square root of a mean is always greater than the mean of the individual square roots. In symbolic notation:

$$\sqrt{(\overline{\delta P})} \; > \; (\overline{\sqrt{\delta P}}) \tag{8.1}$$

Consequently, the square root error leads to exaggerated values of both the mean flowrate and the total volume passed.

(b) *The response time error.* This arises because many types of flowmeter are unable to respond fast enough to changes in flowrate. The most common cause of slow response in flowmeters is the inertia of moving parts or manometer fluids, but, even in flowmeters without moving parts or manometers, response can sometimes be too slow because of the inertia of the flowing fluid, or because of thermal or electrical effects. If the flow pulsates too rapidly for the meter to respond, it will lag behind the actual flowrate and its mean output will not be the true mean flowrate. Usually, though not inevitably, the response time error will tend to make the meter overestimate the flow.

(c) *The asymmetrical error.* This error is peculiar to differential pressure meters and pitot tubes. It occurs if the damping in the two tubes joining the primary to the differential pressure device is not the same. There is a simple cure for it: make the two connecting leads identical.

(d) *The directional effect error.* This is another error affecting differential pressure meters and pitot probes, where tubes are used to connect the primary to the secondary element. If the resistance to flow in these tubes is not the same in one direction as it is in the other direction, the effect when the pressure rises will not be equal and opposite to the effect when the pressure falls again to its original value. In terms of the electrical analogy, 'partial rectification' will occur, and hence the mean differential pressure indicated will not be the true mean.

(e) *The velocity profile error.* Pulsating flow is known to have a distorting effect on velocity profile, although just how much it affects it is still obscure. It follows that those flowmeters which are sensitive to velocity profile alterations will be liable to an additional error of this kind when pulsations occur.

(f) *The resonance error.* This error is altogether different from those previously considered, because it is in the 'all-or-nothing' class. All mechanical flowmeters and most electrical flowmeters have a natural frequency of vibration. If flow pulsations occur at a frequency near that of the flowmeter, it is likely to resonate. Should this happen the flowmeter readings will probably become inaccurate—perhaps wildly so.

8.2.3 The Hodgson Number

In any discussion of the measurement of pulsating flow the term 'Hodgson number' is likely to crop up. Unfortunately it sometimes seems as if some of the engineers who are familiar with the term, and even know how to evaluate a Hodgson number, do not fully understand its significance.

The essential point to grasp is that the Hodgson number has only a limited sphere of usefulness, and it is of much less importance today than it used to be. Hodgson formulated it in the 1920s, when it was necessary to use differential pressure meters to measure the pulsating flow of steam into reciprocating engines. He found that in this and similar circumstances there was an inverse relationship between the total error due to the pulsations and the dimensionless number, H_n, which bears his name[1]. This is defined as:

$$H_n = \frac{Vf}{Q_V} \frac{\delta P}{P} \qquad (8.2)$$

where V is the volume of pipework between the flowmeter and the steam engine
(or whatever is causing the pulsations),

f is the frequency of the pulsations,

Q_V is the volumetric flowrate,

δP is the pressure drop between the flowmeter and the
source of the pulsations, and

P is the absolute pressure at the meter.

Hodgson's work showed that, as long as H_n was greater than 2, the error in an orifice plate was practically always below 1%. A fairly detailed account of the relationship between Hodgson number and the error in differential pressure meters is given in the 1964 edition of BS 1042[2].

It is clear from equation 8.2 that H_n may be increased either by increasing the volume, V, or the pressure drop, δP, between the meter and the cause of the pulsations. This can be done by inserting either a vessel of large capacity or a constriction into the pipework, as shown diagrammatically in *Figure 8.4*. Of these two alternatives, adding a constriction is simpler and cheaper but its effect is more limited than that of the added capacity.

Although the Hodgson number remains a useful indicator of the maximum likely errors in differential pressure meters when severe pulsations are present, it is of little value as a guide to the effect of pulsations on modern flowmeter types such as turbine, ultrasonic, electromagnetic and vortex shedding.

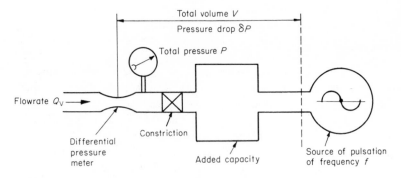

Figure 8.4 *Hodgson number may be increased by adding a constriction or (preferably) a capacity*

8.2.4 What to do About Pulsating Flow

To the flowmeter user flow pulsations are a pest, and like all pests they are something to be eradicated if possible, or at least partially eliminated. If it proves impossible to get rid of them the following rules will help you to live with them.

(a) If possible site the flowmeter a long way from the source of the pulsations, where they will have had time to attenuate.

(b) If the meter has to be installed close to the pulsation source, try inserting a capacity or a constrictor such as a valve, as shown in *Figure 8.4*; this will reduce the severity of the pulsations reaching the meter. In liquid systems, a hydraulic accumulator of the gas-bladder type is much more effective than a simple capacity.

(c) If you are already using a differential pressure meter and do not wish to change to another type, it is possible to get much better results than were possible in Hodgson's day, even at Hodgson numbers far below 2, by proceeding like this. Firstly, obtain an electronic differential pressure cell with a fast response—this will reduce the response time error. Secondly, join it to the meter's pressure tappings with two identical connecting tubes, which should be as short as possible—this will further reduce the response time error, by minimising inertia and compressibility effects in the tubes. Thirdly, connect a high-speed data-processing unit (*see* section 12.4) which is capable of extracting the square root of the signal from the differential pressure cell and then evaluating the mean of the square roots over a period of time—this will practically eliminate the square root error.

(d) If you are prepared to start from scratch and install the best possible flowmeter for the job, bear the following points in mind. (i) Mechanical devices such as turbine meters and rotameters are best avoided, because their inertia causes serious response time errors. (ii) Instruments which depend upon the generation of fluid oscillations, such as vortex-shedding meters, fluidic meters and the Swirlmeter, are risky because of the possibility of resonance. (iii) The possibility of response time errors should be considered before deciding on a meter utilising the tracer principle, such as a Doppler, thermal, cross-correlation, ionisation, or nuclear-magnetic-resonance flow-meter. (iv) Velocity profile errors are inevitable in those flowmeters which are particularly sensitive to variations in profile (but such errors may prove to be rather less serious than most other forms of error caused by pulsating flow). (v) In general, electromagnetic flowmeters (*see* section 6.1) and diagonal-beam ultrasonic flowmeters (*see* sections 6.2.2 and 6.2.3) are likely to give the best results in pulsating liquid flow; but some types are less suitable for pulsating flow than others, so it is essential to consult the manufacturers before purchasing. (vi) For severely pulsating gas flows the use of a fast-response hot-wire probe at the three-quarter-radius position (*see* sections 7.4, 7.5 and 7.8.1)—or, preferably, an array of them across the pipe—could prove more suitable than a full-bore flowmeter, except at fairly limited flowrates where the laminar flowmeter (*see* section 4.5) may be the best solution.

8.3 The Measurement of Two-Phase Flow

The best rule for engineers proposing to meter two-phase flow is like the classic advice to those about to be married . . . Don't!

Wherever possible it is better to separate the gas and liquid phases and meter each on its own. If this is not practicable, then there are some recognised techniques for measuring two-phase flow. However it is important not to over-estimate their worth: they are difficult to apply, and you will have to work very hard at them to obtain an accuracy approaching ±10% in the most favourable circumstances, since accuracies of ±50% or worse are not unknown.

One difficulty is that the gas and liquid phases can arrange themselves in many different ways. Some of the most important patterns of two-phase flow are shown in *Figure 8.5,* but this illustration is by no means exhaustive, since in addition many transitional patterns are possible. There are various methods of predicting which flow pattern is likely to occur under a given set of circumstances, but none of them is foolproof. The sad fact is that much of the time there is no way of knowing just what is going on inside the pipe.

The best chance of obtaining tolerably accurate results occurs when the flow is steady and fairly uniform, as in horizontal stratified flow and horizontal or vertical bubbly flow. As the flow becomes more uneven the accuracy of measurement falls, until in the extreme cases of slug flow and churn flow the results of measurements become almost useless.

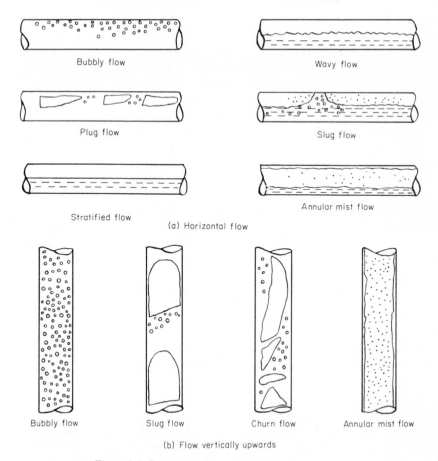

Bubbly flow

Wavy flow

Plug flow

Slug flow

Stratified flow

Annular mist flow

(a) Horizontal flow

Bubbly flow   Slug flow   Churn flow   Annular mist flow

(b) Flow vertically upwards

Figure 8.5 *Some typical two-phase flow patterns*

To sum up, the metering of two-phase flow is not something to be attempted lightly. If you simply have to do it, study the literature[3-6] before you begin, do the best you can to obtain good accuracy—and then treat the results with great caution.

8.4 Metering Cryogenic Liquids

By 'cryogenic liquids' is meant gases that have been liquefied by the application of very low temperatures. The commonest are liquid hydrogen, liquid oxygen, liquid nitrogen, and liquefied natural gas. Their density changes markedly with variations in temperature, and mass flow measurement is therefore usually required.

Recent work has shown that reasonably accurate results can be obtained from various conventional metering systems, provided that (a) cavitation is avoided and (b) the meter is calibrated on a cryogenic flow rig. Volumetric flowmeters found suitable include turbine meters, positive displacement meters and vortex shedders; true mass flowmeters of the angular-momentum type have also given good results[7-9]. Orifice plates can be used too, but are not quite so accurate[9]. Densities may be obtained from densitometers specially designed for making cryogenic measurements.

Calibration of small cryogenic meters is difficult, but possible. Gravimetric[10] and volumetric[11] calibration systems are already giving good results with cryogenic liquids at low and moderate flowrates, and special pipe provers can be used at temperatures down to $-50^{\circ}C$[12]. Unfortunately it is not yet possible to calibrate large cryogenic meters, and the problem of accurately metering liquefied natural gas on a large scale is therefore still awaiting a solution.

8.5 Metering Corrosive Fluids

Metering corrosive fluids is not particularly difficult. Many manufacturers supply flowmeters lined with stainless steel, glass, PTFE, or other corrosion-resistant materials. The only problem is paying the extra cost of these rather specialised flowmeters.

An alternative and more economical approach is to use a clamp-on ultrasonic meter (see section 6.2.6) in situations where the limited accuracy of such devices is acceptable. Remember, it costs no more to fix a clamp-on meter to the outside of a stainless steel pipe (or even a platinum one!) than to a cast iron pipe.

8.6 Metering Potable Liquids

Special meters designed for easy cleaning are necessary where potable liquids such as milk or soup are involved. Some meters are designed so that they can be taken apart very easily at the end of each day, and reassembled after cleaning. Others are intended to be cleaned *in situ,* either by flushing through with a harmless cleaning fluid, or by steam purging; such meters should be designed so that there are no nooks and crannies where stale material could lodge. In addition, meters for potable liquids need to be built with a lining of stainless steel or some other material chosen for its compatibility with the liquid concerned.

8.7 Very Wide Range of Flowrates

As we saw in Chapter 3, the rangeability of a differential pressure meter is small—
at best, no more than 5 to 1. In the early days, when these were the only type of
flowrate meter available, there was only one way to cover a very wide range of
flowrates in one pipeline, and that was by putting 2 or 3 meters of different
sizes in parallel. A later variation on this theme was to build boxes (often referred
to as 'Senior Fittings') around orifice plates, so that several plates with different
area ratios could be used interchangeably in the one box, thus catering for several
overlapping flowrate ranges.

These cumbersome practices are still widespread today, although the necessity
for them has disappeared. Most modern types of flowmeter with their linear output have a rangeability of about 10 to 1, and some of them will perform with
moderate accuracy over a range of at least 30 to 1. (Some manufacturers even
talk of rangeabilities of 100 to 1, but obviously measurements made at 1% of full
scale are unlikely to be very accurate.)

Before contemplating the use of two meters in parallel, see whether one wide-
range meter will do the job. Flowmeter types worth considering for this purpose
include spring-loaded variable-aperture, laminar, positive displacement, Pelton
wheel, bypass, thermal tracer-type, vortex-shedding, and hot-resistor or propeller-
type insertion meters.

8.8 Where to Learn More

The best survey of mass flow measurement methods is still probably that
published by Brain in 1969[13]. The book by Katys[14] contains detailed descrip-
tions of several types of mass flowmeter and discusses their performance.

There is an abundance of published information on the measurement of
pulsating flow. A useful book[14] is devoted to it, and one symposium has 17
papers on various aspects of the subject[15]. A vintage survey paper[16] is still
a useful source of references.

Several key papers on two-phase flow have already been mentioned[3-6],
as well as a selection of important papers on the metering of cryogenic
liquids[7-12].

The metering of corrosive fluids and potable liquids is so highly specialised a
topic that the main sources of information are those flowmeter manufacturers
who make meters for this purpose.

References

1   Hodgson, J. L., 'The laws of similarity for orifice and flow nozzle', *Trans.
ASME,* **51**, FSP-51-42 (1929)

2 *BS 1042 (1964).* Methods for the measurement of fluid/flow in pipes. Part 1: Orifice plates, nozzles and venturi tubes.
3 Wood, J. D. and Dickson, A. N., *Metering of oil–air mixtures with sharp-edged orifices,* Heriot-Watt University, Edinburgh Department
4 Smith, R. V. and Leang, J. T., 'Evaluations of correlations for two-phase flowmeters, three current – one new', *J. Eng. Power,* **97**, 589-595 (1975)
5 Hewitt, G. F., 'Role of experiments in two-phase systems, with particular reference to measurement techniques', *J. Brit. Nucl. Energy Soc.,* **12** No. 2, 213-240 (1973)
6 Kasturi, G., Stepanek, J. and Holland, F. A., 'A review of two-phase flow literature', *Pipes and Pipelines,* **16**, 333-336, 511-514 (1971)
7 Brennan, J. A., Stokes, R. W., Mann, D. B. and Kneebone, C. H., *NBS Technical Note 624: An evaluation of several cryogenic turbine flowmeters,* National Bureau of Standards, Boulder, Colorado (1972)
8 Brennan, J. A., Stokes, R. W., Mann, D. B. and Kneebone, C. H., *NBS Technical Note 605: An evaluation of positive displacement cryogenic volumetric flowmeters,* National Bureau of Standards, Boulder, Colorado (1971)
9 Brennan, J. A., Stokes, R. W., Mann, D. B. and Kneebone, C. H., *NBS Technical Note 650: An evaluation of selected angular momentum, vortex shedding and orifice cryogenic flowmeters,* National Bureau of Standards, Boulder, Colorado (1974)
10 Mann, D. B., 'Cryogenic flow-metering research at NBS', *Cryogenics,* **11**, 179-185 (1971)
11 Deppe, G. R. and Dow, R. H., 'The design, construction and operation of a cryogenic flow calibration facility', *Advan. Cryogenic Eng.,* **8**, 371-377 (1963)
12 Shamp, F. F., 'Accuracy in cryogenic liquid measurements', *ISA Trans.,* **10** No. 3, 219-223 (1971)
13 Brain, T. J. S., 'Mass flow measurement methods', *Metron,* **1** No. 1, 1-6 (1969)
14 Katys, G. P., *Continuous measurement of unsteady flow,* Pergamon, London (1964)
15 *Proc. Symposium on the Measurement of Pulsating Flow,* The Institute of Measurement and Control, London (1970)
16 Oppenheim, A. K. and Chilton, E. G., 'Pulsating flow measurement—a literature survey', *Trans. ASME,* **77**, 231-248 (1955)

9

Choosing the Right Flowmeter for the Job

Human mind like parachute—work best when open.

Chan

9.1 Introduction

In principle there is no room for argument about what 'the right flowmeter for the job' means. The right flowmeter is the one that will do the job adequately at the lowest possible total cost, including initial cost, running costs, and the indirect costs arising from inaccurate measurements and from loss of plant utilisation when the flowmeter is out of action.

By this definition there may be only one type of flowmeter that is right for a particular job, or there may be several; it is certain, however, that there will be many 'wrong' flowmeters for any given situation, either because they will not do the job adequately, or because they are unnecessarily expensive. The purpose of this chapter is to help the user to weed out the many wrong flowmeters and restrict his choice to those that are right, or at any rate, nearly right, for his application (*see* Figure 9.1).

This chapter is concerned only with flowmeters for use in pipes, where the user is confronted with a bewildering variety of types. There is no need to deal with velocity meters in this way, because there the choice is much more limited and, in any case, guidance on choosing one of these is given in Chapter 7.

9.2 Cost-consciousness in Flowmeter Selection

The first thing to decide is whether you really need a flowmeter at all. If you merely wish to know whether the fluid in a pipe is travelling rapidly, or slowly, or not at all, then a flow indicator as mentioned in section 6.6 will probably serve the purpose at minimum cost.

Figure 9.1 *Ch oosing the right flowmeter is not an easy task (photo: NEL)*

If something a little better than this is needed—say, an indication to within 5 or 10% of flowrate—it may still be unnecessary to purchase a meter. You may actually have the makings of a satisfactory flowmeter already installed. For example, if there should happen to be a change of section in the pipework, then a pressure tapping upstream and downstream of the change of section, suitably linked to a differential pressure gauge or manometer, will provide an acceptable type of venturimeter at little cost. Alternatively, if there is a small-radius bend in the system, one pressure tapping on the inside of the bend and another on its outside wall will, when connected to a suitable differential-pressure gauge, utilise the centrifugal forces on the fluid to give a reasonable indication of flowrate. Again, a measurement of pressure loss across a section of pipe where significant losses are occurring—for example, at elbows or tee-junctions—will often serve the same purpose. In all these cases it will be necessary to provide some way of relating the differential-pressure readings to flowrate, either by a rough-and-ready calibration, or by calculation based on simple assumptions, or by relating the differential pressure readings to the known characteristics of the system.

If none of these simple expedients will serve, the time has come to start thinking about the purchase of a flowmeter. It is at this point that the selection table which follows should prove useful.

9.3 A Flowmeter Selection Table

The underlying concept of Table 9.1 is extremely simple. Down the left-hand side are listed 22 requirements which cater for the overwhelming majority of applications likely to arise. Across the top are named all the flowmeter types which have been mentioned in this book in their order of appearance. In each of the 700-odd squares where the rows and columns intersect there is a symbol for, 'Yes', 'No', or 'Maybe', to indicate whether the flowmeter concerned meets that particular requirement.

Filling in some of these squares has been extremely easy. For example, there is no doubt whatever that electromagnetic flowmeters meet the requirement for low head loss and positive displacement meters do not.

However, a great many other squares have presented problems. Take the requirement of very wide rangeability, for instance. How wide is 'very wide'? And what does one do about the big variations in performance which occur within one broad type? Positive displacement meters as a class undoubtedly have a wider rangeability than electromagnetic meters as a class—and yet the best electromagnetic meters are superior in this respect to the worst positive displacement meters.

In deciding upon this and a whole host of other tricky questions I have had to use my own judgement, and put into each square the symbol that seemed most reasonable in the light of all the circumstances known to me. No doubt if another flowmeter specialist had been doing the job he would have put different symbols in quite a lot of squares—and, no doubt, in some instances he would have been justified in doing so*.

The fact is that this table, like most great oversimplifications, has to be used with caution. It attempts the virtually impossible task of summarising six chapters full of information in two pages and the result is bound to be inadequate, even though I have made free use of footnotes to qualify certain generalisations. The table must, therefore, be used like a small-scale map to indicate the general area where solutions might be found, and not to provide the last word on any question.

Treated in this way it can save a great deal of time. Use the table to draw up a short list of 'probables', and, if necessary, a second list of 'possibles'; then go back to the relevant sections of Chapters 3–8 for the detailed information on which to base a final decision.

*In which case he might like to write to me; if he can persuade me that his judgement is correct, I shall be glad to alter the table in the next edition.

Table 9.1 Flowmeter selection table

Key: X Generally suitable, or very useful in certain circumstances ? Worth considering, or sometimes suitable 0 Unsuitable, or not normally applicable *Requirement*	Venturi tube	Orifice plate	Nozzle	Low-loss DP meters	Drag plate	Rotameter (glass)	Rotameter (metal)	Spring-loaded
Water flow	X	X	X	X	?	X	?	X
Suspensions of solids in liquids	0	X[a]	0	0	X	0	X	0
Low viscosity organic liquids	X	X	X	X	?	X	X	X
High viscosity organic liquids	0	X[c]	0	0	X	?	?	X
Gases at pressures close to ambient	X	X	X	X	0	X	0	0
Gases at high pressure	X	X	X	X	X	0	X	X
Very large water pipes	X	0	0	X	0	0	0	0
Very large air ducts	?	0	0	?	0	0	0	0
Very small liquid flows	0	?	0	0	0	X	?	X
Very small gas flows	0	?	?	0	0	X	?	?
Very wide rangeability[m]	0	0	0	0	0	0	0	X
Cryogenic liquids	?	?	?	0	0	0	0	0
Hot liquids	X	X	X	X	X	0	X	X
Hot gases, including steam	?	X	X	X	X	0	X	?
Pulsating flow	?[e]	?[e]	?[e]	?[e]	?	0	0	0
High accuracy measurement of liquid flowrate[p]	?	?	?	?	?	0	?	?
High accuracy measurement of liquid quantity[p]	0	0	0	0	0	0	0	0
High accuracy measurement of gas flowrate and quantity[p]	?	X	X	?	?	0	?	?
Insensitive to poor upstream flow conditions[m]	0	0	0	0	0	X	X	X
Low head loss	X	0	0	X	0	0	0	0
Long life without maintenance or recalibration[m]	X	X	X	X	?	X	X	X
Low initial cost (including essential secondary devices)[m]	0	?	?	0	0	X	0	0

[a] Use only segmental type.
[b] Use only with electrically conducting liquids (e.g. water).
[c] Use only quarter-circle or conical-entrance types.
[d] Hot-resistor, propeller and rotating-vane types only.
[e] Special secondary instrumentation is necessary.
[f] Hot-wire type only.
[g] Only in the medium size range, and only if electrical pulse-generator is fitted.
[h] Only in sizes above about 50 mm diameter, and only if frequently recalibrated, preferably with a dedicated pipe prover.
[i] Refers to mass flowrate only.

Laminar	Pos. disp. (high quality)	Pos. disp. (servo driven)	Turbine	Pelton wheel	Mass-produced rotary	Constrained vortex	'Hoverflo'	Angled propeller	Bypass	Metering pumps	Electromagnetic	Ultrasonic (1 diag. beam)	Ult. (multi-diag. beam)	Ult. (cross-correlation)	Ult. (Doppler)	Vortex-shedding	Fluidic (flowmeter)	Swirlmeter	Nuclear mag. resonance	Thermal (tracer type)	Insertion (¾-radius)	Insertion ('Annubar')	Insertion (v – a integ'n.)	Mass flow (momentum)	Mass flow (Wh. bridge)
0	?	?	X	X	X	X	0	?	X	0	X	X	X	?	X	X	?	0	?	?	X	X	X	0	0
0	0	0	0	0	0	?	X	X	0	?	X[b]	?	?	X	X	?	0	0	X	0	0	0	0	0	0
0	X	X	X	X	?	X	0	?	X	0	0	X	X	X	X	X	X	0	X	?	?	?	0	X	X
0	X	X	?	0	0	?	X	X	0	X	0	?	?	?	?	?	?	0	X	0	?	0	0	?	X
X	X	?	?	0	0	0	0	0	0	0	0	0	0	0	0	?	0	?	0	X	X	X	X	0	0
X	X	X	X	0	0	X	0	0	X	0	0	0	0	0	0	X	0	X	0	X	X	X	?	?	0
0	0	0	0	0	0	0	0	0	?	0	X	?	X	0	0	0	0	0	0	0	X	X	X	0	0
0	0	0	0	0	0	0	0	0	0	0	0	0	0	0	0	0	0	0	0	0	X	X	X	0	0
0	?	?	?	X	?	?	0	0	0	0	X[b]	0	0	0	0	0	X	0	0	X	0	0	0	0	X
X	0	0	0	0	0	0	0	0	0	0	0	0	0	0	0	0	0	0	0	X	0	0	0	0	0
X	X	X	0	X	?	0	0	0	?	?	?[b]	?	?	?	?	X	?	X	0	X	X[d]	0	0	0	X
0	X	0	X	0	0	0	0	0	0	0	0	?	?	?	?	X	?	0	0	0	0	0	0	X	0
0	?	0	?	?	0	?	X	X	X	?	X[b]	?	?	?	?	?	0	0	?	?	?	?	?	X	0
?	0	0	?	0	0	?	0	0	X	0	0	0	0	0	0	?	0	?	0	?	X	X	?	0	0
X	0	0	0	0	0	0	0	0	0	0	X[b]	X	X	0	0	0	0	0	0	?	X[f]	0	X[f]	0	0
0	X[g]	X	X[h]	0	0	0	0	0	0	0	?	?	X	0	0	?	?	0	?	0	0	?	?	?[i]	X[i]
0	X[j]	X	X[h]	0	0	0	0	0	0	0	?	0	?	X	0	0	0	0	0	0	0	0	0	0	?
X	X	X	X	0	0	0	0	0	0	0	0	0	0	0	0	?	0	X	0	0	0	?	0	0	0
?	X	X	0	X	?	?	X	0	0	X	?	0	?	0	0	0	?	?	0	0	0	?	?	0	X
0	0	X	0	0	0	0	0	0	0	0	X[b]	X	X	X	X	0	0	0	X	X[k]	X	X	X	0	0
?[q]	?	?	?[l]	?	X	?	?	?	?	?	X[b]	X	X	X	X	X	X	X	X	X	?[n]	?	?	?	?
0	0	0	0	X	X	?	0	0	?	0	0	?	0	0	?	?	0	0	0	0	X[n]	?	0	0	0

j Accuracy of very small and very large meters is less good than that of medium-sized meters.

k However, there is a substantial consumption of thermal energy, which increases with increasing size of meter.

l Turbine meters for gases are better in this respect than those designed for use with liquids.

m Note that it is easier for moderate-accuracy instruments to meet this requirement.

n Depends on the type.

p Note that a higher standard of accuracy is generally called for in the metering of liquids than of gases.

q Depends upon the standard of cleanliness and the maintenance of filters.

10

Pitfalls, and How to Avoid Them

Start her up and see why she don't go.

John Kris

10.1 Bad Installation Conditions

10.1.1 The Extent of the Problem

One thing must be made plain at the outset: the way a flowmeter is installed matters a lot.

Some of the provisions in standard specifications and manufacturers' instruction books read like a counsel of perfection—which, in many cases, they are. However, the rules about not siting a flowmeter too close to a bend a valve, or any other fitting likely to create disturbed flow conditions at the meter, should be obeyed implicitly if accurate measurements are required. This is because flowmeters are always calibrated on the assumption that they will be installed at the downstream end of a long length of straight pipe, and if this assumption is invalidated the meter's calibration factor will be altered.

A vast amount of experience has shown that this is so. To cite just one instance, a flow nozzle had to be installed in a very confined space and it was impossible to avoid putting it close downstream of a pair of bends, as shown in *Figure 10.1*. These conditions were bad, but they could have been a lot worse. After all, the two bends were in the same plane, which is a considerably less serious situation than if two adjacent bends are in two planes at right angles (*see* section 1.2.4), and there was a length of about 10 diameters of straight pipe between the nearest upstream bend and the nozzle.

Even so, the users wisely decided to send the nozzle to NEL for calibration complete with all its contorted upstream and downstream pipework. As

126

Figure 10.1 *Nozzle with contorted upstream pipework undergoing calibration. The arrow indicates direction of flow (photo: NEL)*

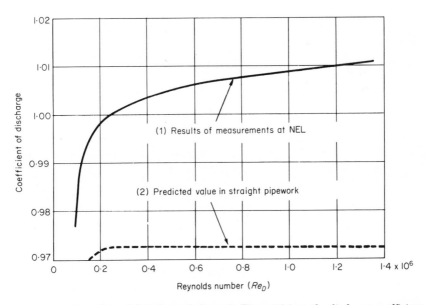

Figure 10.2 *The effect of the pipework shown in Figure 10.1 on the discharge coefficient of a nozzle*

Figure 10.2 shows, the actual coefficient of discharge over the normal working range of the nozzle was between 3 and 4% higher than the usual coefficient for such a nozzle.

Although the effect of upstream flow disturbances is more drastic with some types of flowmeter than others, it can be quite serious with almost any type of accurate flowmeter except positive displacement meters; and there is no reliable way of predicting what the effect of a given pipe configuration upon a given flowmeter is likely to be, because the fluid mechanics of such situations is highly complicated and is not yet fully understood. Time after time experiments in this field have led to unexpected conclusions.

For example, the results of two experiments on orifice plates are shown in *Figures 10.3* and *10.4*. One would expect that the sharper the bend, the greater the error it would cause on an orifice plate—which, as *Figure 10.3* shows, is actually the case so far as bends of radius 1.0*D*, 1.5*D* and 4.75*D* are concerned,

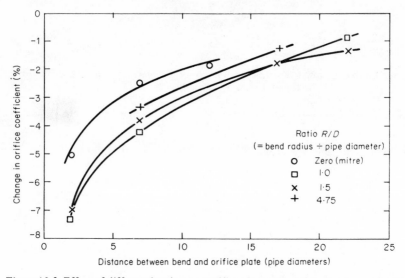

Figure 10.3 Effect of different bends on an orifice place with corner tappings and with
m = 0.64

but not with a mitre (zero radius) bend, which actually caused less error than even the most gradual bend. Again, it would be expected that the orifice plate error would increase with the angle of swirl, but as *Figure 10.4* shows this is true only with orifice plates of large area ratio.

Most of the published work on the effect of upstream flow conditions relates to differential pressure meters. (A small selection of these publications is given in References 1–5.) Although knowledge is still incomplete there is enough data to allow the inclusion of 'minimum distance' tables in the standard specifications

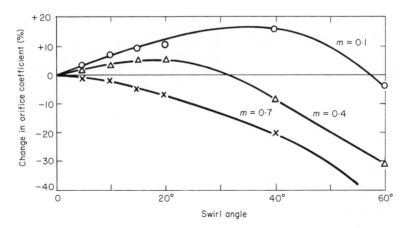

Figure 10.4 *Effect of swirl on orifice plates with three different area ratios*

for differential pressure meters (*see* section 3.1.3). Every flowmeter user should familiarise himself with these tables, and must be prepared to face the unpalatable fact that the required distances for avoiding significant errors are in many cases quite substantial.

Unfortunately there is very much less information on the minimum upstream lengths required in various circumstances by flowmeters of other types. It is usually necessary to ask a manufacturer if he has any experimental data of this kind relating to his own meters. If he is not able to supply a satisfactory answer (and in many cases he will not be), then the table for orifice plates with area ratio 0.5 in the standards mentioned above can be used as a rough guide for other types of flowmeter. But remember: this really is only a very rough guide, since some types of meter will require longer distances whilst others might be satisfactory with less. And if swirl is present (*see* section 1.2.4) meters particularly sensitive to it, such as turbine meters, will require *much* longer distances.

10.1.2 Disturbances on the Downstream Side

Intuitively one might imagine that once a fluid has gone through a flowmeter it does not matter what happens to it. Alas, this is a common misconception. Disturbances caused by a bend, valve, etc., can propagate backwards—against the current—for a few diameters, and so affect flowmeters installed close upstream of them.

It is for this reason that the standard codes also give information on the minimum length of straight pipe required downstream of various differential pressure devices. These are much less than the upstream lengths required: in most cases 5 diameters downstream is sufficient, but occasionally it may be necessary to have a longer length. It can safely be assumed that 10 diameters of straight pipe downstream of the meter is enough to cover every contingency.

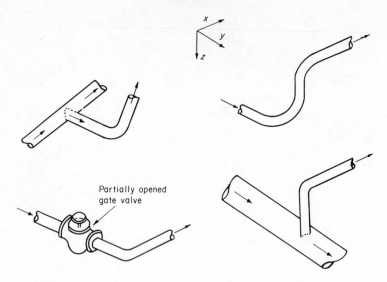

Figure 10.5 *Three-dimensional pipe configurations creating severe swirl*

10.1.3 Rules for Avoiding Installation Errors

Positive displacement meters are unique in their ability to tolerate severely disturbed flow: most of them can safely be installed in pipework shaped like spaghetti. However, with all other flowmeters the following rules should be obeyed if accurate results are to be obtained.

(a) Remember that swirl is the worst enemy. Above all, try to avoid the classic swirl-generating situations where the flow is made to make a three-dimensional bend—that is, to turn two successive right angles in two perpendicular planes, as shown in *Figure 10.5*—within 100 diameters upstream of a meter.

(b) If at all possible install a flowmeter with adequate lengths of straight pipework of the correct diameter upstream and downstream. For differential pressure meters the standard specifications specify what is meant by 'adequate'; for other meters the requirements are less precisely known, but it can safely be presumed that, so long as rule (a) above is followed, lengths of 50 diameters upstream and 10 downstream are sufficient for even the most susceptible types of flowmeter. Some types will tolerate much less, but unless you know what your meter requires it is best to err on the safe side.

(c) If it is impossible to accommodate the desirable lengths of straight pipe there are two alternatives. Either have the flowmeter calibrated after it has been installed in its pipework, complete with all the nearby bends, valves, etc.; or install a flow straightener, taking care to follow the guidelines given below.

10.2 The Use of Flow Straighteners

10.2.1 Which Type?

As the name suggests, the primary purpose of a flow straightener is to remove swirl and not to correct a distorted velocity profile. Some types of straightener are designed to improve a badly shaped profile as well as to reduce swirl, but other types do not have a very beneficial effect on a bad profile and often they may actually make a fairly good profile worse.

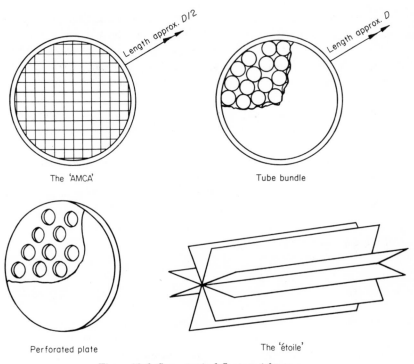

Figure 10.6 *Some typical flow straighteners*

The four most usual types of straightener are shown in *Figure 10.6*. They each have their own good and bad points. The tube bundle is very effective at reducing swirl and fairly good at correcting an asymmetrical velocity profile, but it creates a substantial pressure loss (at least 2 velocity heads) and tends to flatten a correctly shaped profile.

The AMCA and étoile straighteners are good at removing swirl but not at correcting asymmetry, and the flow leaving them is liable to have a somewhat distorted profile. Their great advantage is that they produce only a negligible head loss.

The perforated plate is greatly inferior to the other three as a swirl remover but it is much better at correcting asymmetry. It possesses the unique advantage of being easy to install, since it can be slipped between a pair of flanges. However, the pressure loss it causes—at least 5 velocity heads—renders it unacceptable in many installations.

A high performance is claimed for the Zanker flow straightener[6], but it is not very widely used because it is expensive and creates a high head loss.

10.2.2 Guidelines for Installing Flow Straighteners

If a flow straightener is carelessly installed it can sometimes do more harm than good. It is essential that the following guidelines should always be followed.

(a) The perforated plate will do its job even if it is positioned very close to the source of the flow disturbance. It should therefore be inserted in the flanged joint at the downstream end of the valve, bend or fitting that is causing the trouble.

(b) All other types of straightener need to be inserted at least 3 diameters downstream of the source of the disturbance, because otherwise they are liable to be swamped by the freshly generated disturbance.

(c) Because the profile of the flow emerging from a straightener is always distorted, there must be enough straight pipe between the straightener and the flowmeter for most of the distortion to disappear. Ideally this intervening length could be as much as 20 diameters and it should not be less than 10 diameters unless the flowmeter is to be calibrated *in situ,* in which case 5 diameters is acceptable.

10.3 Cavitation

Most flowmeter users are aware that if cavitation (*see* section 1.2.7) occurs inside a flowmeter this will cause it to give erroneous readings. When this occurs it is inevitably the result of insufficient pressure at the meter. It can be prevented by installing a back-pressure valve downstream of the flowmeter, and using it to ensure that the meter pressure never falls below the minimum value stipulated by the standard specifications or the meter manufacturer.

But there is also another danger which is much less commonly recognised. If cavitation occurs in some fitment upstream of the meter this also can cause metering errors. This is because cavitation, especially if it occurs in oils, fuels and solvents, releases a cloud of bubbles which may persist for quite a long distance downstream. The worst offenders are flow-control valves, which are liable to cavitate whenever they are left in the nearly closed position, and certain types of three-way and four-way valves, which tend to produce a burst of cavitation whenever they are changing position.

It is worth remembering that a relatively small volume of bubbles can give rise to quite substantial errors. Tests have shown that 1% of bubbles in the liquid entering a turbine meter may cause it to over-read by as much as 5%. Furthermore it does not take many bubbles to block the pressure tappings of a differential pressure meter and thus throw it completely out of true.

10.4 Entrained Air

In the previous section it was noted that cavitation can generate small air bubbles in a liquid, which are liable to cause metering errors. There are several other ways in which air can lead to errors in liquid flow metering, however, which can be lumped together under the broad description of air entrainment. They generally give rise to air pockets of larger size than the fine bubbles produced by cavitation. This is fortunate, because large pockets of air are relatively easy to remove from a flowing liquid before it enters a flowmeter, and it is often cheaper to do this than to prevent air from being entrained in the first place.

The main causes of air entrainment are discussed below in sections 10.4.1–10.4.4, and finally in section 10.5 methods of removing air pockets automatically are described.

10.4.1 Air Trapped when Filling a System

When a pipework system has been shut down and drained of liquid for maintenance, it can sometimes be quite a difficult task to fill it again. Pockets of air are liable to lodge in all the high spots in the system, such as the tops of inverted U-bends, only to break up and pass through the system in gulps at some later date when the flowrate or the pressure happens to fluctuate suddenly.

This trouble should not occur in a well designed system, where high spots will be few and where those that do exist will each be provided with an air bleed, through which the operator can vent the trapped air at the time of filling the system. In a system with many high spots it may be too much trouble to vent them all. The alternative is to provide an air separator (*see* section 10.5) upstream of the flowmeter and rely upon this to deal with any gulps of air that may come along the pipe.

10.4.2 Leaking Seals

It is surprisingly easy for air to be sucked into a pipe at a joint where the seal is only slightly defective. Air is so much less viscous than any liquid that a seal which is adequate for keeping liquid inside a pipe can be hopelessly inadequate for keeping air out. It is not only the joints in suction lines that are vulnerable in this respect although obviously the danger is greatest there, but also joints in pipes just above atmospheric pressure can sometimes allow air to be sucked in, if pulsations should produce momentary sub-atmospheric pressures in the line.

In metering systems where there is no air separator it is desirable for all pipe joints in suction lines to be inspected occasionally, and for their seals to be replaced at the first sign of damage.

10.4.3 Tanks Running Low

When a supply tank runs low, so that the head of liquid above the inlet to the suction pipe is only a few pipe diameters, a vortex of the bath-tub variety is liable to form and cause a stream of air to enter the suction pipe. This is probably the commonest and most serious cause of air entrainment that the flowmeter user is likely to meet.

Tank designers use various expedients to lessen the danger of 'bath-tub' vortex formation. These include the putting of the suction pipe outlet in a small well below the tank bottom, and all sorts of anti-vortex baffles. However, none of them is foolproof, and whenever a supply tank is likely to be drained nearly dry the inclusion of some sort of air separation device is therefore essential. It is for this reason that every kerbside metering petrol pump must, by law, be fitted with an air separator.

10.4.4 Contraction During Cooling

This is a rather subtle form of air entrainment. When a system is shut down overnight the pipes full of liquid will cool. The difference in thermal expansion coefficients will make the liquid contract much more than the pipework, and when this causes the liquid to pull away from the pipework air will be drawn out of solution to fill the resulting vacuum. The net result will be that in the morning there will be air pockets at the top of all the pipes; if the temperature change has been $15°C$, these air pockets could amount to about 1% of the liquid volume.

In a system where valuable liquids are being metered for sale these air pockets must not be allowed to pass through the meter, since this would lead to the first customer in the morning being defrauded. Consequently, in all such systems there must be some provision for disposing of the air pockets formed by overnight contraction. Sometimes this can be achieved by manual bleeding of the air pockets when the system is started up, but it is more usual—and more foolproof—to let an air separation device do the work automatically.

10.5 The Use of Air or Gas Separation Devices

10.5.1 Introduction

It will have been apparent from the previous sections that air entrainment is a very common problem, and that a variety of air separation devices are in use for dealing with it.

In fact the use of such devices, although widespread, is limited to certain fields. They are hardly ever used in conjunction with flowrate meters, because these are normally installed in continuously operating systems where air entrainment is not a major difficulty. Nor are they used where water quantity is being metered, since here the value of the product is too low to justify the extra expense. But their use is obligatory in many situations where valuable liquids, and especially petroleum products, are being metered intermittently for the purpose of trade or taxation. Such applications include kerbside metering petrol pumps, metering systems on road tankers, and metering systems at depots where delivery vehicles are loaded.

10.5.2 Principal Types of Air Separation Device

There are three main types of air separation device, each fulfilling a different purpose. Until recently only one of them had a descriptive name in English, presumably because the other two types were less commonly used in Britain and the USA than on the Continent. However in 1977 an EEC Directive[7] was issued in several languages, which officially gave names to all three types. The names used in the English version of this directive will probably gain general acceptance in course of time, and so they might as well be used here and now.

(a) *The gas separator.* This is the device most likely to be familiar to English and American readers, who have been accustomed to calling it an 'air eliminator', 'air separator', or 'deaerator'. It usually consists of a fairly large pressure vessel, often with some internal baffles added *(Figure 10.7)*. This reduces the flowing liquid to a snail's pace and gives the entrained air plenty of opportunity to rise to the top of the vessel. Here the air is vented through a valve controlled by a float, which prevents any liquid from escaping.

Other types of gas separator utilise centrifugal force to expedite the passage of air through the liquid. These are usually more compact than the gravity-operated types described above.

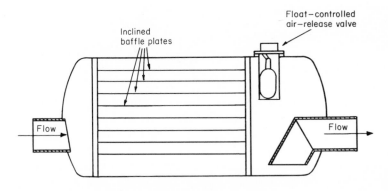

Figure 10.7 *Typical gas separator*

Gas separators are heavy-duty devices. They are designed to deal effectively with all forms of air entrainment, and will even remove a proportion of any cavitation bubbles that may come their way.

(b) *The gas extractor.* This is a simple inexpensive device, built like a smaller version of the gas separator of *Figure 10.7* (but probably with its axis vertical) and without the internal baffles. It is not capable of removing the large quantities of air which arise through vortex entrainment, especially if this air happens to occur in the form of small bubbles rather than large gulps. The gas extractor is intended solely for the much lighter duty of removing pockets of air formed during filling of the system (*see* section 10.4.1) or as a result of contraction during cooling (*see* section 10.4.4). It should never be used in systems where either vortex entrainment or cavitation might occur.

(c) *The special gas extractor.* This is intended to provide a compromise between the compactness of the gas extractor and the reliability of the gas separator. It consists basically of a gas extractor coupled to an electrically operated shut-off valve. As long as only small quantities of air are entering, the device operates as if it were an ordinary gas extractor. However, if an exceptionally large quantity of air should overwhelm it this will not pass into the flowmeter, because as soon as the special gas extractor starts to fill with air it activates the electrically operated valve and stops the flow.

10.5.3 *Points to Watch When Using*

(a) The flow leaving a gas separation device is severely disturbed, and the rules of section 10.1.3 must therefore be applied. Originally, these devices were used only in association with positive displacement meters, which are not affected by flow disturbances. Nowadays they are being used increasingly with other types, such as turbine meters, where serious errors can result if the separator is too close to the meter.

(b) The air issuing from the vent valve will certainly be saturated with vapour, and probably will carry droplets of liquid too. If the liquid concerned is a fuel this can present a fire hazard. The air should therefore be piped away to a safe place—preferably to the space at the top of the supply tank from which the liquid is being drawn.

10.6 Condensation

The phenomenon of water vapour condensation in gases was described in section 1.1.6. The metering errors it causes are usually not large, but they are quite large enough to make it important to avoid condensation whenever air or gas is being metered to the highest possible standards of accuracy.

The surest way of avoiding it is to dry the gas. This is often impractical, and it may be simpler to control the pressures and/or the temperature in the test circuit so that saturation conditions are never reached.

10.7 Wear and Dirt

A flowmeter is a scientific instrument and needs to be treated as one. It is curious that many an engineer will take his wristwatch to be cleaned and oiled once a year, but is quite content to leave his flowmeters in the line for years and years, and expects them to go on giving accurate readings until they pack up completely.

This is particularly true of differential pressure meters, because, so the legend has it, there is nothing that can go wrong with them. In fact the combined effects of corrosion, erosion and deposits of dirt can sometimes change their coefficient of discharge—and hence their accuracy— by several per cent over the years. They should be inspected at reasonable intervals, and as soon as it is apparent that a meter is not what it used to be the user should have it recalibrated or replaced. In particular, the edges of orifice plates should be examined for signs of bluntness (*see* section 3.6f).

With turbine meters the commonest causes of error are bearing wear and small deposits of dirt or shreds of fibre adhering to the blades. Less common, but by no means rare, are errors caused by bent blades or worn blade edges. Similar problems can arise with propeller-type current meters and vane anemometers, the thin blades of the latter being very easily bent.

When electromagnetic meters are not fitted with self-cleaning electrodes there is always a danger that dirt will accumulate on the electrodes and produce errors. Regular inspection is an essential safeguard.

10.8 Over-ranging

Most types of rotating flowmeter, including turbine meters and positive displacement meters, can be damaged if the flowrate should rise well above their designed

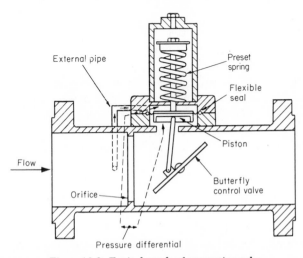

Figure 10.8 *Typical overload-prevention valve*

maximum. If there is much risk of this happening, even momentarily, an overload-prevention valve should be installed in the system.

A valve of this kind is illustrated in *Figure 10.8.* If the flowrate should exceed a specified value the differential pressure generated by the main orifice forces the piston down against the spring, thus moving the butterfly towards the closed position and restricting the flow. A well designed overload-prevention valve will not hunt between two extreme positions, but will settle at a position of stable equilibrium with the flowrate controlled at an almost constant value.

10.9 Spurious Electrical Signals

10.9.1 Nature of the Problem

The readout of many modern flowmeters is in the form of a train of electrical pulses. With such meters the pulse frequency can be used as an indication of flowrate, but the more common practice is to use the number of pulses collected by an electronic counter to indicate the total volume passed.

If total volume is to be measured correctly with such a system it is important to prevent spurious pulses from being counted, since these will cause the system to over-read. Unwanted pulses can enter the measuring system either through the electrical mains ('supply-borne noise') or through cables acting as aerials and picking up electromagnetic radiation ('air-borne noise'). Both forms of noise must be excluded if high accuracy metering is intended.

Moreover, in many situations it is desirable for there to be some way of testing the system to ensure that the counts being obtained really are free from spurious pulses. Various methods of achieving this are available. The most positive method is to use meters fitted with dual pulse-generation systems, so that the outputs from the two systems can be compared (*see* section 5.3.1). A useful check can be made from time to time by operating all the electrical equipment in the vicinity, including hoists and hand tools, while no flow is passing through the meter. If the counter should register any pulses under these conditions, this is a sign that electrical interference is occurring.

If the whole metering system is provided by one manufacturer, it is reasonable in the first place to put the onus upon him to ensure that it is fitted with the necessary protection. Interference problems are usually at their worst in systems assembled by the user. However, whether you buy your system as a whole or couple together the units yourself, it is still important to be aware of the way to safeguard against false counts.

10.9.2 Rules for Minimising Spurious Pulse Counts

What follows is not a complete set of rules for building and operating a foolproof system—that would take far too much space to give here. Instead, a few basic rules for avoiding the commonest and most serious sources of error are given. Manufacturers of high-precision metering systems generally follow these rules;

unfortunately, users who are unaware of them sometimes undo the manufacturer's good work by making unauthorised alterations to the system. So it pays to bear the following points in mind.

(a) Avoid picking up supply-borne noise by using mains filters on all mains-powered instrumentation.

(b) Preamplify a signal before transmitting it. (Most high-quality pulsed-output flowmeters will have preamplifiers built in.) It stands to reason that an amplified signal will be distorted less by a given level of noise than the same signal before amplification.

(c) If the pulses are a poor shape, pass them through a signal conditioner before they enter the counter.

(d) Always transmit signals in screened cable, and ensure that the cable sheath is grounded at one point only so as to prevent the formation of ground-loops.

(e) Keep signal-transmission cables and power supply cables as far apart as possible, and if they have to cross, then make them cross at right angles.

(f) Avoid using parallel-lay cables for data transmission; cables made of individually twisted pairs are the least liable to pick up airborne noise, but helical-lay cables are usually acceptable.

(g) Pulse counters, signal conditioners, and amplifiers are made with different response times. Do not use equipment with a much faster response than is needed for the maximum pulse frequency of the system, because high-speed instruments pick up electrical noise more readily than slower ones.

(h) Keep an eye open for bad connections and worn or damaged components.

10.10 Safety

It is important always to remember that a flowmeter is a potential source of weakness in a pipe. The manufacturer's instructions for fitting the flowmeter in the pipe, connecting any secondary instruments, and making electrical connections, must all be scrupulously observed if accidents are to be avoided. In particular three very obvious points are noted below, simply because neglect of them has in the past led to accidents.

(a) Every flowmeter has a specified pressure and temperature rating. To exceed *either* of these is to invite a burst, since hot materials are less strong than cold ones.

(b) Corrosion progressively weakens a flowmeter, as well as impairing its accuracy. It is dangerous to use a mild steel meter for high-pressure duty in a corrosive environment.

(c) In an area where flammable liquids and gases are being used, all electrical equipment must be specially designed so that it cannot cause a fire or an explosion. If a flowmeter or its accessories are electrically operated and were supplied for ordinary duty, they will probably be unsafe (and illegal!) if put to use in an area of high fire risk where only officially approved devices are permitted.

10.11 Where to Learn More

For information on the effect of installation conditions see the references cited above[1-5], also the standard specifications on differential pressure meters mentioned in Chapter 3 and those on turbine meters mentioned in Chapter 5. An early survey paper on flow straighteners[8] is still a useful source of information. Recent work on the effect of upstream disturbances on turbine meters has been reported by Hutton[9] and by Tan[10].

Advice on avoiding cavitation bubbles and entrained air in circulating oil systems is given in a booklet by the author[11]. Information on various air separation devices is in the EEC Directive referred to[7].

There appears to be little published information on the effect of dirt, corrosion and wear on metering accuracy; one exception is a paper by Hutton[12] dealing with their effects upon venturimeters.

A code of practice for avoiding spurious pulse counts is published by the Institute of Petroleum[13], and a similar code is likely to be published soon by the ISO. For detailed information on safety precautions, it may be necessary to refer to various government regulations, but for many purposes the Code of Safe Practice drawn up by the Institute of Petroleum[14] will prove sufficient.

References

1 Pardoe, W. S., 'The effect of installation on the coefficients of venturimeters: Final Report', *Trans. ASME,* **65** No. 4, 337–359 (1943)
2 Sprenkle, R. E., 'Piping arrangements for acceptable flowmeter accuracy', *Trans. ASME,* **67** No. 5, 345–360 (1945)
3 West, R. G., 'The problems of non-standard installations and some general conclusions', *Instrument Practice,* **15** No. 8, 973–981 (1961)
4 Ferron, A. G., 'Velocity profile effects on the discharge coefficient of pressure differential meters', *J. Bas. Eng.,* **85** No. 3, 338–346 (1963)
5 Blake, K. A., Kennedy, A. and Kinghorn, F. C., 'The use of orifice plates and venturi nozzles in swirling or asymmetric flow', *IMEKO VII, Paper BFL 240,* Institute of Measurement and Control London (1976)
6 Zanker, K. J., 'The development of a flow straightener for use with orifice-plate flowmeters in disturbed flows', *Flow measurement in closed conduits,* HMSO, Edinburgh, 395–415, 472–477 (1962)
7 *Council Directive 77/313/EEC of 5 April 1977, on the Approximation of the Laws of the Member States Relating to Measuring Systems for Liquids Other than Water*
8 Sprenkle, R. E. and Courtright, N. S., 'Straightening vanes for flow measurement', *Mech. Eng., N.Y.,* **80** No. 2, 71–72 (1958); **80** No. 8, 92–95 (1958)

9   Hutton, S. P., 'The effect of inlet flow conditions on the accuracy of flow-meters', *Component interactions in fluid flow systems,* CP9-1974, Institution of Mechanical Engineers, London, 1-8 (1975)

10 Tan, P. A. K., 'Effects of upstream disturbances and velocity profiles on turbine flowmeter performance', *Sixth Thermodynamics And Fluid Mechanics Conf.,* Institution of Mechanical Engineers, London, 71-79 (1977)

11 Hayward, A. T. J., *How to keep air out of hydraulic circuits,* National Engineering Laboratory, East Kilbride, Glasgow (1963)

12 Hutton, S. P., 'The prediction of venturimeter coefficients and their variation with roughness and age', *Proc. Inst. Civ. Eng., Part 3,* 3, 216-241, 922-927 (1954)

13 *Petroleum Measurement Manual, Part XIII, Section 1.* Code of practice for the security and fidelity of electric and/or electronic pulsed data transmission systems for the metering of fluids. Institute of Petroleum, London (1976)

14 *Institute of Petroleum model codes of safe practice in the petroleum industry—Part 2, Marketing safety code.* Heyden and Sons, London (1978)

11

How to Calibrate Flowmeters and Velocity Meters

> *CALIBRATE, verb trans:*   *Find calibre of*
> *CALIBRE, noun:*   *Internal diameter of gun*
>
>   Concise Oxford Dictionary
>   (1946 edition)

Where anything more than a moderate standard of accuracy is required, flow-meters need calibration. Sometimes, as in the case of large turbine meters used for the fiscal metering of petroleum, the meters may have to be calibrated every day against a built-in calibration device. At the other extreme, some meters may only need to be taken out of the line for calibration once every couple of years or so, in which case the user will probably prefer to send them to an independent laboratory rather than to maintain his own calibration facilities.

Either way it is useful for every flowmeter user to know something of the calibration techniques in common use, of which all the more important ones are described below.

11.1 Methods of Calibrating Flowmeters with Liquids

11.1.1 Volumetric Tank Used in the Standing-Start-and Finish Mode

This method *(Figure 11.1)* is particularly suited to the calibration of total quantity meters, such as the positive displacement meters commonly used for metering oils and fuels. It is not suitable for use with flowrate meters, or with instruments such as turbine meters which permit large quantities of unregistered fluid to slip past at low flowrates.

At the start of a calibration the pipework from the pump to the base of the volumetric tank is completely filled with liquid, the stop valve is in the closed position, and the dial of the meter is on zero. Then the pump is started, after

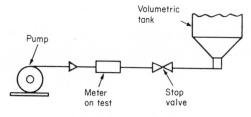

(a) Principle of the method

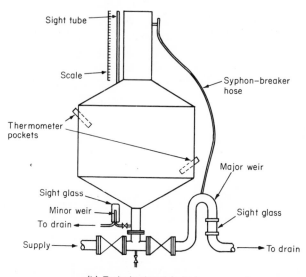

(b) Typical volumetric tank

Figure 11.1 *Calibration by the standing-start-and-finish method, using a volumetric tank*

which the valve is opened as fast as possible and allowed to remain open until the volumetric tank is full, when it is rapidly closed. For accurate results, steady flow should exist during at least 99% of the duration of the test. The indication of 'total volume passed' on the dial of the meter at the end of the test is compared with the volume known to have flowed into the volumetric tank, after making any necessary corrections for thermal expansion in both the liquid and the tank.

Volumetric tanks of many different designs are in use, of which one of the most common is illustrated in *Figure 11.1b*. This design ensures that the level of liquid in the bottom neck of the tank at the start of a test is always the same, and the calibrated scale against the sight tube at the top of the tank enables the operator to read directly the quantity passed into the tank during the test. Tanks of this type are supplied as a standard commercial item. Other designs are also in use in which the tank is filled from the top.

An accuracy of ±0.05% of total volume measurement is easily obtainable with this method, and if great care is taken higher accuracies should be possible.

11.1.2 Gravimetric Tank Used in the Standing-Start-and-Finish Mode

A cheaper alternative to a volumetric tank for standing-start-and-finish calibrations is a gravimetric system. This can easily be assembled by the user, who merely needs to provide a tank sitting on a weighing machine as shown in *Figure 11.2,* and to arrange for it to be filled with a 'swan-neck' constant-level device as shown.

The main difficulty in using such a system is that the density of the test fluid must be known for each calibration, so that the weight reading (after applying a correction for air buoyancy) can be converted to a volume. This is a very simple procedure when the test fluid is water, whose density does not change rapidly with changes in temperature, and can be determined from tables after making a temperature measurement. Hydrocarbon fuels, however, have a high coefficient of thermal expansion, and having to determine their density accurately on each occasion is a nuisance when this method is used. On the other hand, viscous hydrocarbon oils cannot readily be used with a volumetric tank because they cling to the walls of the tank, and this problem is eliminated when

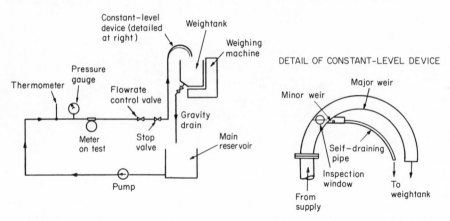

Figure 11.2 *Calibration by the standing-start-and-finish method, using a gravimetric tank*

a gravimetric tank is used instead.

On balance, if it is intended to use a standing-start-and-finish method of calibration, it is probably better to use the gravimetric method if the test fluid is water or a viscous oil (above, say, 5 cSt), and to use a volumetric tank with low viscosity hydrocarbons (below, say, 5 cSt).

An accuracy of ±0.05% of total volume determination can be obtained, provided that sufficient care is taken to measure densities accurately.

11.1.3 Gravimetric Flying-Start-and-Finish Method, with Static Weighing

This method is widely used when flowrate meters have to be calibrated with water. It is less appropriate for the calibration of total volume meters, or for meters which are being calibrated with oils or fuels.

The test liquid after passing through the flowmeter passes through a control valve and into a fishtail which produces a fan-shaped jet; as shown in *Figure 11.3* a diverter is arranged so that this jet can be made to pass at will into either a reservoir or a weightank. A switch fitted to the diverter plate is connected to an electronic timer, which indicates the length of time during which the flowing jet

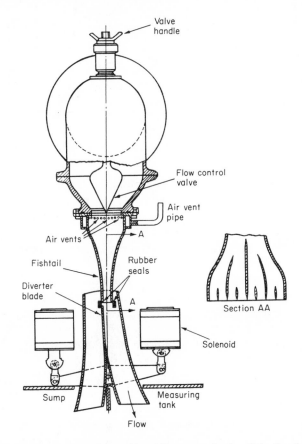

Figure 11.3 *A typical assembly of flow control valve, fishtail and diverter*

is diverted into the weightank. The gravimetric flowrate is equal to the mass collected in the weightank divided by the diversion time, and this can be converted to a volumetric flowrate by dividing it by the density of the test liquid at the appropriate temperature.

Because it takes a finite time for the diverter to pass through the flowing jet, the times at which diversion is said to begin and end must be chosen arbitrarily. That is to say, the mechanical switch attached to the diverter blade which starts and stops the timer must be set at some precise points in the travel of the diverter, which are shown as E and H in *Figure 11.4*. Bearing in mind that the

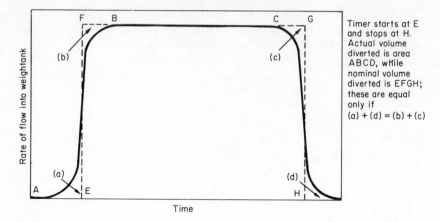

Figure 11.4 *Variation of flowrate entering weightank in a flying-start-and-finish calibration*

area under a flowrate/time graph is equal to total volume, it is evident that when the first diversion (into the weightank) takes place, some liquid (volume a) passes into the collecting tank before the timer starts, and some liquid (volume b) passes into the sump instead of the weightank after the timer has started. If the timing switch is correctly positioned, these two volumes, (a) and (b), will be identical and therefore self-compensating.

Similarly, in the final diversion (out of the weightank at the end of the test) there will again be two volumes (c) and (d) which should be self-compensating if the timer switch is correctly positioned. Because the motion of the diverter and the shape of the flowing jet are not likely to be entirely symmetrical, it is fallacious to imagine that the correct position for the timer switch is at the geometrical centre of the diversion. The ideal position for the switch can only be obtained by experiment.

In such an experiment the flow must be set to a constant value, and a number of diversions of alternately short and long duration must be made. Then the measured flowrate can be plotted against the reciprocal of the diversion time as shown in *Figure 11.5a.* If the line joining the experimental points is sloping, as in this figure, this shows that the timer switch is incorrectly set and must be adjusted. When the setting of the switch is right the line joining the experimental points will be horizontal as in *Figure 11.5b.*

Failure to set diverter switches correctly in this way causes inaccuracy in many flow calibration systems of this type. In a well designed system the correct setting for the switch will be independent of flowrate, but in some systems when a timer switch is set correctly for high flowrates it is in the wrong position for low flowrates. The experiment described above to check the correct setting of the timer switch should therefore always be carried out at both high and low flowrates.

If care is taken to set the diverter trigger correctly to measure density accurately and to service and recalibrate the weighing apparatus at regular intervals, an accuracy of ±0.2% in flowrate measurement can be attained.

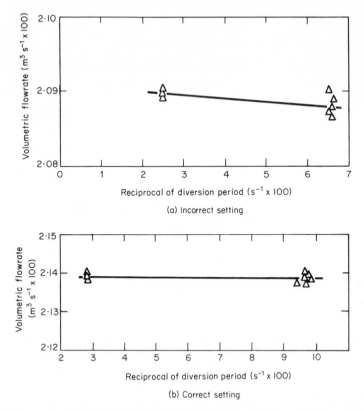

Figure 11.5 *Results of diverter adjustment tests carried out at NEL: (a) diverter trigger incorrectly set, (b) diverter trigger correctly set*

11.14 Gravimetric Flying-Start-and-Finish Method, with Dynamic Weighing

This method *(Figure 11.6)* is employed chiefly for the calibration of flowrate meters at low and moderate flowrates. At very high flowrates inertia effects are likely to create unacceptable errors.

After passing through the flowmeter on test the liquid falls into a weightank, and to begin with it passes out from the weightank through the opened dump valve at its base. When a test is required, the dump valve is quickly closed, whereupon the level in the weightank begins to rise. As soon as it reaches a certain preset value, the electrical output from the weighing machine automatically starts a timer and/or flowmeter pulse counter. The level in the weightank continues to rise, and when another value of weight is reached the timer and/or pulse counter are automatically stopped by the weighing machine output. To avoid the possibility of overflowing the tank it is convenient if the dump valve is then automatically opened by the same electrical impulse, operating after a short preset delay.

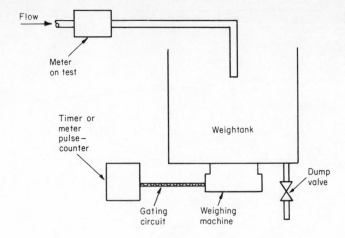

Figure 11.6 *Principle of the dynamic weighing method*

For accurate results the liquid entering the weightank must do so as a vertical free-falling jet, the weightank must have vertical walls, and its overall height should not be much greater than its width or breadth. Also, the weighing machine must not be affected by the inertia of the weightank being much greater when it is full than when it is empty. This last requirement can best be met by using a load-cell type of weighing machine.

The dynamic weighing method lends itself to the 'substitution' or 'comparator' method, which is illustrated in *Figure 11.7*. In this method an accurately known weight sits on the weighing machine beside the weightank, and this weight is removed after the rising level in the weightank has automatically started the timer. Another automatic circuit stops the timer when enough liquid has entered the

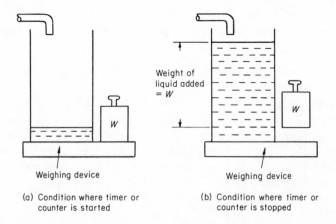

Figure 11.7 *Principle of the 'substitution' or 'comparator' method of dynamic weighing*

tank to compensate for the loss of the weight which has been removed. In this way the total 'before' and 'after' inertias of the weightank system are identical, and the weighing machine is, in effect, recalibrated every time a test is carried out. Thus weighing errors are kept to a minimum and the maximum calibration accuracy is obtained. It is not difficult to measure flowrate with an accuracy of ±0.2% by this means.

11.1.5 Pipe Provers

Pipe provers are used very widely in the petroleum industry and to a limited extent elsewhere, for the accurate calibration of liquid quantity meters and especially of large turbine meters. They are extremely expensive to install, but very convenient and rapid in operation, and consequently have low operating costs. They also have the advantage of possessing a higher repeatability than any other device for calibrating liquid flowmeters. Although they can be used with flowrate meters, in practice their use is largely confined to the calibration of quantity meters. Large petroleum metering stations frequently have a pipe prover permanently built in; it is then known as a 'dedicated prover'.

There are several types of pipe prover, of which currently the most popular is the bi-directional sphere-type *(Figure 11.8)*. A hollow sphere of synthetic rubber is inflated with water under pressure until its diameter is about 2% larger than that of the epoxy-lined pipe from which the prover is constructed. When the sphere is forced into the pipe it seals it, and acts as a kind of piston which is capable of going round bends. A four-way valve is used to control the flow of liquid after it has passed through the meter which is to be calibrated, by causing the liquid to travel through the prover either from left to right or from

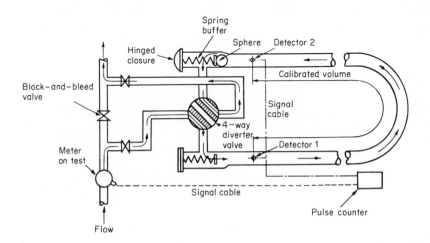

Figure 11.8 *Principle of the bi-directional pipe prover*

right to left. At either end of the prover there is a chamber of enlarged diameter to receive the sphere at the end of each trip.

Prior to a calibration run the flow is allowed to bypass the prover. At the start of a test the flow is directed through the prover in such a way that the sphere travels the whole length of the prover. Soon after the start of its run it passes a sphere detector, which operates an electrical gating circuit and causes the electrical pulses from the meter on test to be counted.

Near the end of the run a second sphere detector is operated which stops the count of pulses. The pulse count from the meter is then compared with the known volume of the prover between sphere detectors, which has been deter-mined from a previous static calibration of the prover. Additional accuracy is gained by totalising the pulse counts and the prover volumes during two succes-sive runs, one in each direction. Directional effects in the sphere detectors are thus largely cancelled out.

The accuracy of the bi-directional prover when it is maintained in first-class condition may be as high as ±0.1% on flowrate, and between ±0.05 and ±0.02% on total volume.

In the uni-directional sphere-type prover *(Figure 11.9)* the sphere travels round the prover in one direction only, and always returns to its starting point through a sphere-handling valve. Because it is not possible in this type to eliminate directional effects in the sphere detectors, the uni-directional prover is slightly less accurate than the bi-directional type.

A third alternative is the bi-directional piston-type prover, which employs a long length of straight pipe and a metal piston with elastic seals instead of a sphere. This type generally occupies more space than the sphere-type provers, because of the need for a long length of straight pipe with subsidiary connecting pipework, and is rather more expensive. For this reason it is mostly used in special circumstances, for instance, where refrigerated liquids or very hot liquids are being used, or in situations where very high accuracy is required and expense

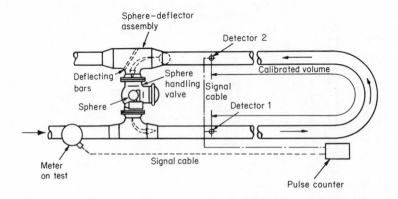

Figure 11.9 *Principle of the uni-directional pipe prover*

is no object. Some early piston-type provers employing ordinary pipeline 'pigs' travelling in ordinary pipe are still in use, but this simple type of piston prover is generally regarded as obsolescent nowadays.

A proprietary variant on the piston-type is known as a ballistic flow calibrator. It employs compressed air from a separate source to propel the piston and thus displace liquid from the calibrator through the meter on test. Its use is largely confined to small fuel meters, in applications where moderate flowrate variations during the test can be tolerated.

Another proprietary type of piston prover utilises a glass tube containing a loosely fitting piston, at the centre of which an annular ring of mercury, held in place by surface tension, acts as a practically frictionless seal. It is used specifically for calibrating very small gas flowrate meters.

11.1.6 Master Meters

The simplest and cheapest way of calibrating a flowmeter is to put it in series with another flowmeter of higher accuracy and to compare their readings. This can give reasonably accurate results over a short period, provided that care is taken to install the two meters sufficiently far apart to ensure that the downstream meter is not affected by the wake from the upstream meter. A serious disadvantage of the method is that the performance of the master meter will itself gradually change with time; consequently, recalibration of the master meter will be needed at intervals.

Also, if the master meter should suffer any kind of sudden mechanical wear its performance could change markedly in a very short period without the operator being aware that anything was amiss. As a safeguard against this happening it is possible to use two master meters in series (again, taking care to ensure that the downstream meter is not affected by the wake from the upstream meter) as shown in *Figure 11.10*. As long as the two meters continue giving the same reading the operator can be fairly confident that all is well, but as soon as

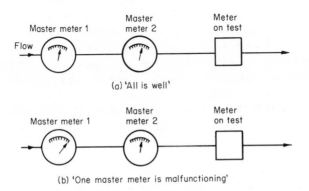

Figure 11.10 *The use of two master meters in series*

one master meter gives a significantly different reading from the other he knows that one meter is malfunctioning. The rig must then be shut down while both meters are removed for recalibration.

To avoid having to shut down the rig in circumstances like this, three master meters can be installed in series. In this case, the malfunctioning meter will immediately betray itself by showing that it is out of step with the other two. The defective master meter can then be taken out of the line and sent away for recalibration, while the operator continues to use his rig with the other two master meters in operation.

A third alternative is to use two master meters in parallel, with high-fidelity shut-off valves, as shown in *Figure 11.11*. This system is suitable only when

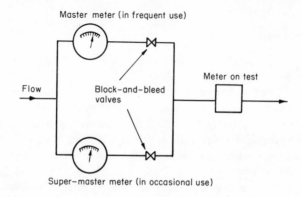

Figure 11.11 *The use of two master meters in alternate parallel*

meters of high repeatability, such as large turbine meters, are to be calibrated, because the meter on test provides the only way to compare the performances of the two master meters. One master meter is used as the main calibration device, with the other master meter, denoted in *Figure 11.11* as a 'super-master meter', being used alternately with the first master meter on infrequent occasions as a check that the master meter remains unchanged. As soon as a change in the performance of the master meter is observed it is removed for recalibration, after which it is regarded as the supermaster meter, while the other meter then becomes regarded as the master meter until such time as another recalibration is called for, when the roles of the two meters are again reversed.

A well maintained master meter calibration system should, if based on the best available meters, provide accuracies of ±0.2% (or, in special circumstances, ±0.1%) on flowrate, and ±0.1 or ±0.05% on volume.

11.1.7 Combination of Master Meter and Calibrator

A very convenient method of calibrating flowmeters is obtained by installing a master meter in combination with one of the calibration devices described above.

The meter can then be calibrated against the calibrator at frequent intervals to ensure that its characteristics have not changed, and meanwhile the meter can be used to calibrate flowmeters directly. In this way the accuracy of the basic calibration device is combined with the speed of operation and convenience of the master meter. Moreover, if the master meter is of the positive displacement type and has a high-frequency pulse-generator fitted to it, and if the calibrator

Figure 11.12 *Combination of volumetric standard and master meter (photo: Moore, Barrett and Redwood Ltd.)*

is of the standing-start-and-finish variety (sections 11.1.1 and 11.1.2), then the master meter can be calibrated by this highly accurate method and subsequently used in flying-start-and-finish tests to calibrate flowrate meters. In this way, a reasonably inexpensive calibration system for flowrate meters can be obtained, with an accuracy of ±0.1% on flowrate, which is probably unattainable with any other system of comparable cost.

This method is particularly useful when a portable calibration system is required, since both calibrator and master meter can be mounted on one vehicle or trailer, as shown in *Figure 11.12.*

11.1.8 Indirect Methods for Calibration at High Flowrates

The calibration devices described above become prohibitively expensive when very high flowrates—say, above about 1 m^3 s^{-1}—have to be dealt with. In this range indirect methods of calibrating flowrate meters are much less costly.

Both the tracer-velocity and tracer-dilution technique described in section 6.5.1 can be used for the calibration *in situ* of very large flowrate meters. Various types of tracer, each with an appropriate detection system, can be used: dyes, detected by colorimeters or fluorimeters; salt solutions, detected by conductivity meters or by chemical analysis; and radioactive materials, detected by radiation meters. Skilled operators can measure flowrates by these means with an accuracy of ±1%, or perhaps ±0.5% under the most favourable conditions.

Velocity–area integration techniques as described in section 7.9 are also used for calibrating large flowrate meters to an accuracy of ±1%.

11.1.9 Points to Watch when Calibrating Liquid Flowmeters

(a) Good upstream flow conditions are even more essential in a calibration circuit than elsewhere; pay special attention, therefore, to the recommendations in section 10.1.3. If necessary, carry out a velocity traverse at the entry to the test section to check that there is a good velocity profile there,

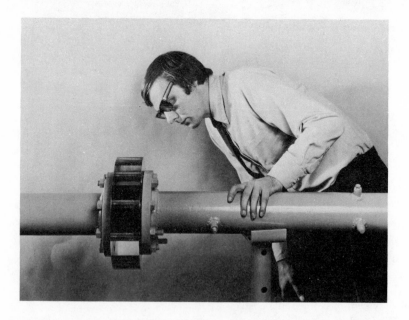

Figure 11.13 *A sight-piece of transparent plastics for the detection of bubbles and pockets of air in a liquid calibration system (photo: NEL)*

and use a multi-hole pitot probe or a laser velocimeter to verify that there
is no swirl.

(b) Steadiness of flow is also important. If possible, the test section should
be fed by gravity from a constant-head tank; if the supply is directly from
a pump be sure that the pump used has a steady output. Keep the number of
pipe bends—and especially, sharp bends—to a minimum. Pulsations of high
frequency can sometimes be reduced to an acceptable level by inserting a
coarse wire-mesh screen into the pipework at a flanged joint well upstream
of the test section.

(c) Avoidance of bubbles in the test section is essential. Follow the rules for
avoiding cavitation (section 10.3) and air entrainment (section 10.4). A ring-
shaped sight-piece of transparent plastic inserted between two flanges, as
shown in *Figure 11.13,* provides a convenient way of confirming that no air
is present in the flowing liquid.

(d) When a gravimetric method is used, a correction for air buoyancy must
be made in order to convert weight into mass of liquid. Failure to do this will
introduce a systematic error of about 0.1%.

11.2 Methods of Calibrating Flowmeters with Gases

11.2.1 Soap Film Burettes

The soap-film burette *(Figure 11.14)* is the gasman's counterpart of the pipe
prover described in section 11.1.5. It is suitable only for low flowrates, since it is
difficult to form a stable soap film across a burette of more than about 50 mm
diameter. The film is made to act as a frictionless 'piston' which travels freely

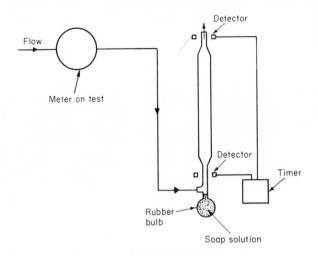

Figure 11.14 *Principle of the soap-film burette*

with the flowing stream of gas, so that the velocity of the film is a good indication of the velocity of the flowing gas.

The soap-film burette can be used to calibrate both flowrate and quantity meters. It will measure flowrate with an accuracy of ±0.5% and volume with an accuracy between ±0.5 and ±0.2%.

11.2.2 Bell Provers

The bell prover, as shown in *Figure 11.15*, is analogous to the volumetric standing-start-and-finish method of section 11.1.1. In this method a previously calibrated cylinder is lowered into a bath of water at a controlled rate, thus displacing a known volume of gas through the meter on test. Like all standing-start-and-finish methods it is best suited to the calibration of total quantity meters, although if the bell used is large enough the acceleration and deceleration errors can be ignored in a calibration of a small flowrate meter. Physical limitations on size restrict the use of the bell prover to fairly small meters, such as domestic gas meters. It will deliver its stipulated volume with an accuracy approaching ±0.2%, under the most favourable conditions of operation.

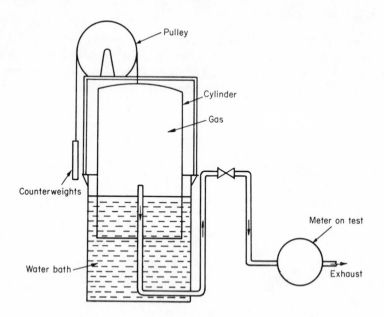

Figure 11.15 *Simplified schematic arrangement of bell prover system for calibrating small gas quantity meters*

11.2.3 The Hyde Prover

The Hyde prover is probably the most accurate device available for calibrating small gas quantity meters, since an accuracy of ±0.1% is claimed for it. It consists essentially of a metal pipette-shaped vessel with a volume of approximately 30 litres which is enclosed in a constant temperature bath. Water is used to displace a known volume of air from this vessel through the meter on test.

This is essentially a tool for standards laboratories, because its operation calls for considerable skill and experience.

11.2.4 Sonic Venturi-Nozzles

The sonic venturi-nozzle *(Figure 11.16)*, or critical-flow venturi-nozzle as it is sometimes called, is a very convenient device for calibrating a gas flowrate meter at one volumetric flowrate. It depends upon the fact that in the throat of a nozzle the gas cannot travel faster than the speed of sound. Provided the upstream pressure is sufficient to ensure that sonic velocity is actually reached, the flowrate through the nozzle will therefore always have a fixed value for a given gas at a specified temperature and pressure. The tapered venturi section downstream of the nozzle plays no part in controlling the flowrate; its function is merely to assist in recovering some 90–95% of the initial pressure, thus conserving energy.

If a number of sonic venturi-nozzles of various sizes are used in succession a gas flowmeter can be calibrated over a range of flowrates with them. When the highest possible accuracies (about ±0.5% on flowrate) are called for it is usual for the venturi-nozzles to be calibrated against a primary gas flow standard before they are used as calibration devices. If slightly lower accuracies are acceptable their performance can be predicted fairly reliably from a knowledge of their dimensions.

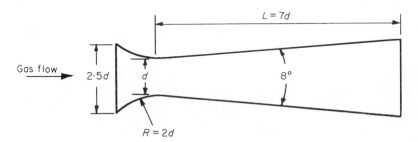

Figure 11.16 *Standard sonic venturi-nozzle*

11.2.5 Gravimetric Flying-Start-and-Finish Gas-meter Calibrator

The gravimetric flying-start-and-finish calibrator is a highly sophisticated and expensive device, but is regarded as the best available primary system for calibrating secondary high-pressure gas flow standards. It can also be used directly for the calibration of high-pressure gas meters. It is broadly similar in principle to the gravimetric flying-start-and-finish system with static weighing for liquids described in section 11.1.3, but with one important difference: in the liquid system the meter being calibrated is upstream of the flow diverter, but in the gas system it is downstream and in a line venting to atmosphere. This enables the meter to be read under steady-state conditions, thus overcoming the problem of diminishing flowrate which occurs while the weighing vessel is being filled.

As shown in *Figure 11.17* a critical venturi-nozzle is used to maintain a constant flowrate through the test system. In the first part of the test the flow downstream of this nozzle is diverted through the meter being calibrated, while

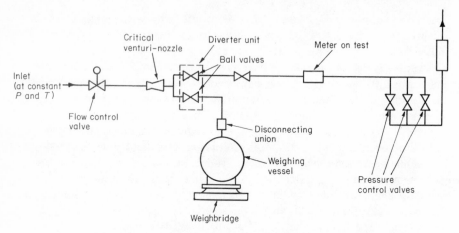

Figure 11.17 *Simplified arrangement of a gravimetric system for compressed gases*

its reading is noted. Then the flow is diverted into a lightweight spherical pressure vessel for a measured time, and the measurements of the weight of this sphere before and after diversion are used to calculate the mass flowrate during the diversion period. By varying the pressure upstream of the critical venturi-nozzle a fairly wide range of mass flowrates can be covered with this system, and by using several alternative nozzles of different sizes an almost unlimited range can be obtained.

The accuracy of flowrate measurement in a system of this kind is between ±0.5 and ±0.2%.

11.2.6 PVT *System*

The *PVT* (pressure–volume–temperature) method is used mainly as a primary standard, to calibrate reference meters and sonic venturi-nozzles which can thereafter be used as secondary calibration devices. In this system, illustrated in *Figure 11.18*, a storage vessel of known volume is charged with gas at high

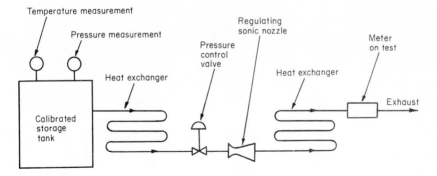

Figure 11.18 *Principle of the PVT system for calibrating gas meters*

pressure. The pressure and temperature of the gas in the vessel are first measured, then the gas is allowed to flow out through a regulating sonic nozzle in series with the meter on test, and finally the pressure and temperature of the gas in the storage vessel are measured again at the end of a measured period of time.

From these measurements the mass flowrate through the system during the test period can be calculated. Heat exchangers and an upstream pressure controller are used to control the conditions during flow and thus the performance of the meter on test can be determined over a wide range. Accuracies of flowrate measurement between ±0.5 and ±0.2% can be achieved.

11.2.7 Master Meters

Master meters are frequently used for calibrating other gas meters. A useful combination is obtained by linking a calibration device such as a bell prover (section 11.2.2) or a Hyde prover (section 11.2.3) to a wet gas meter (section 5.2.5), which can then be easily recalibrated at frequent intervals. By this means the accuracy of the prover can be combined with the convenience of the master meter.

It is possible to extend greatly the range that can be covered with one prover by using it in conjunction with a very large gas bag and a fairly small wet gas master meter. In this way a large gas meter can be calibrated by passing the flow from it into the gas bag. When this bag has been filled it can subsequently be collapsed by the application of external pressure, so as to expel the gas through the wet gas master meter which was previously calibrated against the prover. In this way the small master meter operating at a relatively low flowrate is used indirectly to calibrate the meter on test, which shortly before had passed the same total mass of gas at a much higher flowrate.

The wet gas meter is a total volume meter and its use as an accurate master meter is therefore restricted to total volume meters. Used directly its accuracy can be in the region of ±0.25%; used along with a gas bag as described in the previous paragraph, the overall accuracy is probably limited to about ±0.5%.

Flowrate meters such as orifice plates are sometimes used as master meters to calibrate other gas flowrate meters, the accuracy being between ±1 and ±0.5%. However, they look like being displaced from this role by critical nozzles, which will do much the same job rather more effectively.

11.2.8 Tracer Methods

Tracer-velocity and tracer-dilution techniques as described in section 6.5.1 can also be used for calibrating gas flowrate meters. Radioactive tracers have considerable advantages over other types of tracer when used with gases, and they are now the most widely used types. Their main disadvantage is that handling radioactive materials safely is a job for experts, and calibrations by this method are usually carried out by nuclear physicists.

Under favourable conditions flowrate can be measured in this way with an accuracy of ±0.5%.

11.2.9 Pitot Traversing

A useful method of calibrating medium-sized or large flowrate meters with air at pressures near ambient is that of pitot traversing, followed by velocity–area integration (*see* sections 7.2 and 7.9). The advantage of this method is that it requires only the relatively simple equipment shown in *Figure 11.19,* and this makes it particularly suitable for general laboratory use.

The accuracy obtainable by a skilled operator is about ±1%.

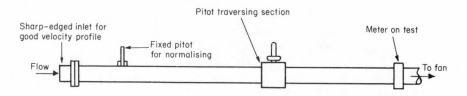

Figure 11.19 *Typical pitot traversing system for calibration with air at ambient pressure*

11.2.10 Points to Watch when Calibrating Gas Flowmeters

(a) Because they have such a big effect on gas density, the pressure and temperature in a gas-meter calibration system must be measured very accurately. Variations with time and with position in the system must be studied and allowed for, if necessary.

(b) Pulsations can be a serious problem. Fans and compressors with good delivery characteristics should always be selected for flowmeter calibration systems, and stilling chambers and/or screens should be added if necessary to attenuate any severe pulsations which cannot be eliminated at the source.

(c) Avoid condensation, as advised in section 10.6.

(d) Avoid bad upstream pipework conditions by following meticulously the rules of section 10.1.3. In installations like that of *Figure 11.19*, where the flow conditions should be well-nigh perfect, do not make the all-too-common mistake and spoil things by putting the sharp-edged inlet too close to the floor, the ceiling, a wall or an obstruction—or by letting a careless experimenter stand nearby!

11.3 Calibrating Velocity Meters

Calibrating a fluid velocity meter is either a very easy job or a very difficult one.

It is difficult if one wishes to start from scratch and make an absolute calibration. For current meters this normally involves fixing them to the travelling carriage of a ship-testing tank, and observing their performance when moving

Figure 11.20 *A pitot tube being calibrated in a free jet of air (photo: NEL)*

through still water at a known speed. Anemometers are usually fixed to the end of a long rotating arm and moved around a toroidal duct. In both cases corrections have to be made to allow for the fact that the test conditions during calibration are not the same as those when the meters are subsequently used, and the whole procedure becomes rather complicated. So it is just as well that such determinations are normally carried out only in a few national laboratories.

The ordinary user will almost certainly calibrate his velocity meters the easy way. That is, he will purchase an anemometer probe or a current meter which has been calibrated at a national laboratory and use this as a master velocity meter against which to calibrate his own working meters.

Calibration then consists of placing the two velocity measuring devices, master and working, one after the other in the same stream of air or water and comparing their readings. Fluctuations in the stream velocity are allowed for by 'normalising' as described in section 7.9.2. A pitot tube is shown being calibrated in a free jet of air in *Figure 11.20*.

11.4 Where to Learn More

A survey paper on methods of calibrating flowmeters with liquids was published by the author[1], and a parallel paper on calibrating gas meters by Brain[2]; both of these contain useful bibliographies. Standards on velocity-area integration methods were mentioned in section 7.10 and a series of ISO standards on the use of tracers for measuring flow have recently been published[3].

The whirling-arm method of calibrating anemometers has been described by Cowdrey[4], and the towing-tank method of calibrating current meters is covered by an ISO standard[5]. Pipe provers are the subject of an API standard[6] and a simple code of practice issued by the IP[7]. There are useful papers on soap-film burettes[8], sonic venturi-nozzles[9] and a gravimetric gas calibration system[10]. The American Society for Testing and Materials[11] and the Instrument Society of America[12] have both published codes of practice for calibrating rotameters. Hyde has described his prover in the book by himself and Jones[13].

The procedure for calculating the air buoyancy correction required for converting weight to mass is given in Kaye and Laby[14] along with a table of values.

References

1   Hayward, A. T. J., 'Methods of calibrating flowmeters with liquids—a comparative survey', *Measurement and Control,* **10** No. 3, 106–116 (1977)

2   Brain, T. J. S., 'Reference standards for gas flow measurement', *Measurement and Control,* **11** No. 8, 283–288 (1978)

3   *ISO Standard 2975* (Water flow—in seven separate parts) and *ISO Standard 4053* (Gas flow—in four separate parts)

4   Cowdrey, C. F., 'A note on the calibration and use of a shielded hot-wire anemometer for very low speeds', *J. Sci. Instrum.*, **27** No. 12, 327–329 (1950)

5   *ISO Standard 3455 (1976)*. Liquid flow measurement in open channels— calibration of rotating-element current meters in straight open tanks

6   *API Standard 2531 (1963)*. Mechanical displacement meter provers (now being superseded by Chapter 4.2 in the new API Manual—*see* section 13.2.2

7   *A field code of practice for proving turbine and displacement meters with prover pipes,* Institute of Petroleum, London (1979)

8   Harrison, P. and Darroch, I. F., *NEL Report No. 302, Air flow measurement by the soap-film method,* National Engineering Laboratory, East Kilbride, Glasgow (1967)

9   Hillbrath, H. S., 'The critical flow venturi: a useful device for flow measurement and control', *Symposium on Flow, 1971,* Paper No. 1-3-205, American Society of Mechanical Engineers, New York (1971)

10 Collins, W. T. and Selby, T. W., *Report No. K-1632, A gravimetric gas flow standard—Parts 1 and 2,* Union Carbide Corp., Nuclear Division, Oak Ridge (1965)

11 *ASTM Standard D 3195-73*. Recommended practice for rotameter calibration

12 *ISA Standard RP 16.6 (1961)*. Methods and equipment for calibration of variable area meters (rotameters)

13 Hyde, C. G. and Jones, M. W., *Gas calorimetry,* 2nd edn., Ernest Benn, London, 76 (1960)

14 Kaye, G. W. C. and Laby, T. H., *Tables of physical and chemical constants,* Longman's, 14th (revised) edn., London (1975)

12

Instrumentation used with Flowmeters

Big bugs have little bugs upon their backs to bite 'em.
The little bugs have littler bugs—and so ad infinitum.

Author unknown

This is an enormous subject which really needs a book—or, rather, a series of books—to itself, and this chapter must therefore have a very limited aim. This is firstly to deal with a few matters of special importance to flowmeter users, such as the design of piezometer rings and thermometer pockets, secondly to give some idea of the great variety of equipment now available, and thirdly to offer a few practical tips on the use of some of the devices most commonly found in flow metering situations.

12.1 Pressure and Differential Pressure Measurement

12.1.1 Pressure Tappings and Piezometer Rings

A pressure tapping needs to be drilled carefully. The hole should break through the inner wall of the pipe at right angles and with a clean sharp edge, since a small chip or burr at this point can cause a significant error[1]. The diameter of the hole should be small, because a large tapping hole can interfere with the flowmeter geometry and cause errors[2]; but it must not be so small that it will easily become blocked.

In pipes with diameters above about 100 mm it is desirable to use four equi-spaced tapping holes on one cross-section and join them together with tubing to form a piezometer ring. In this way a mean of the pressures at the four tappings is obtained, and the individual errors due to non-ideal conditions at each tapping are largely cancelled out. It has recently been shown[3] that the conventional method of piping piezometer rings *(Figure 12.1a)* does not give

164

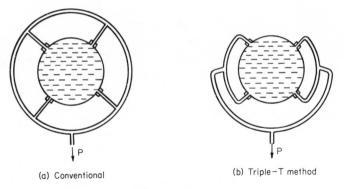

(a) Conventional   (b) Triple–T method

Figure 12.1 *Two forms of piezometer ring*

a true mean because of circulation around the ring, and that significantly
better results are given by the 'Triple-T' method of *Figure 12.1b.*

12.1.2 U-tube Manometers

The U-tube filled with liquid was the earliest device used for measuring differential pressure. Filled with mercury it will measure differentials up to about 2 bar,
or with water up to about 0.2 bar. Converting manometer heights into pressures
can involve a lot of tedious computation, in which the density–temperature
function of the manometer fluid plays a part. The ISA manometer tables[4] will
cut out most of the labour from such calculations.

Although it is now obsolescent in most industrial situations, the simple
U-tube manometer with either vertical or sloping limbs is still an important
laboratory tool, and in recent years it has appeared in a number of new guises,
as mentioned below. These more elaborate forms of U-tube are all available
commercially, often in several widely different forms from different manufacturers.

(a) *Electrical-readout mercury manometer.* A number of electrical
displacement-measuring devices have been fitted to mercury manometers so
that the differential height is indicated automatically. This enables the high
accuracy of the mercury manometer (up to ±0.1% of full scale in ordinary
circumstances) to be combined with the ability to transmit data in electrical
form. They are now declining in popularity for industrial use, because
differential pressure transducers (*see* section 12.1.4) are gradually catching
up with them in accuracy and are much more compact and convenient in
use, and often less costly.

(b) *High-pressure mercury manometer.* A logical development of the mercury
manometer described above is to put it inside a strong steel tube so that it can
be used to measure relatively small differentials at high line pressures. In this

form its main use is as a primary laboratory standard, for the calibration of both secondary standards and working differential pressure transducers.

(c) *Optical projection manometer.* In the course of measuring air flow, very small pressure differentials have to be measured with high accuracy. One way to do this is to use a water-filled (or, possibly, oil-filled) manometer in which the differential height is indicated with high accuracy by an optical projection system.

(d) *Tilting manometer.* Another instrument designed for high-accuracy aerodynamic work is the null-balance tilting glass U-tube. After the (small) applied differential has caused the water (or oil) level in the two limbs to alter, the level can be restored by tilting the tube. Various ingenious systems are used for measuring the angle of tilt in such a way that this can be used directly as a measure of the applied pressure differential.

(e) *Ring-balance manometer.* This is an offshoot of the tilting manometer described above. It is designed for use at high line pressures so that the tube must be made of steel, and it is therefore not possible to see the position of the liquid in the tube. This difficulty is overcome by making the tube toroidal— that is, ring-shaped—and pivoting it on a knife-edge at its centre; when an applied differential causes the liquid levels to move this unbalances the ring, and a counterweight sliding on the ring must be moved to restore the balance. The magnitude of the differential pressure can then be determined with high accuracy from the position of the counterweight. This is essentially a primary standard which is used for calibrating secondary differential pressure standards. A low-pressure variant of this device is made from transparent plastic and filled with oil.

12.1.3 Bourdon Gauges

The Bourdon pressure gauge is another venerable device which has recently been subject to a striking new development.

A normal Bourdon gauge depends upon a metal tube with an oval cross-section which has been bent into a near-circular shape. When the pressure inside the tube is higher than that outside it tends to straighten the tube to some extent. A mechanical system of linkages converts this partial straightening into the rotation of a needle on a dial, thus producing the familiar conventional pressure gauge.

Bourdon gauges can be constructed as differential pressure gauges, if one of the two pressures is connected to the inside of the bent tube and the other to an enclosure surrounding the tube. Alternatively, two Bourdon tubes carrying the two separate pressures can be linked mechanically so that their net effect on the indicating needle is proportional to the differential pressure. Gauges of this kind can be employed with differential pressure meters in installations where convenience is more important than accuracy, although this usage is not very common.

In a much higher class there is the quartz-tube differential pressure Bourdon gauge, which is a laboratory instrument of high accuracy against which other differential pressure instruments can be calibrated. A helical Bourdon tube of fused quartz gives more repeatable results than a metal tube, and the performance is further enhanced by replacing the mechanical linkage system of the ordinary Bourdon gauge with an optical lever system operating a digital counter. Repeatabilities of ±0.1% can be obtained when measuring small differentials at a line pressure of several kilobar, but since this apparatus is a secondary standard its absolute accuracy depends upon the accuracy with which it has been calibrated against a primary standard. A rather similar device is the 'Digigauge', which employs a metal capsule instead of a quartz Bourdon tube. It is slightly less accurate, but is robust enough for use as a portable calibration device in the field.

12.1.4 Transducers

At the heart of a typical differential pressure transducer is a small metal diaphragm of perhaps 20 mm diameter, with a small chamber on each side to which the two pressures are connected. The deflection of the diaphragm is monitored by some means incorporated in the transducer; this may be a strain gauge or a variable-capacitance or variable-reluctance device. In this way an electrical analogue output proportional to the pressure difference across the diaphragm is obtained.

Because the overall size of the transducer is small it can easily be built to withstand extremely high line pressures, if necessary. An overload protection device is usually incorporated to prevent the diaphragm from rupturing if the full line pressure should accidentally be applied to one side. These features make transducers very suitable for connection to differential pressure meters in high-pressure systems, and especially where an electrical output is required.

One disadvantage is that the characteristics of differential pressure transducers are to some extent affected by the magnitude of the line pressure. Where the highest possible accuracy is required they should be calibrated against an appropriate primary or secondary differential pressure standard at the line pressure at which they are to be used. For industrial purposes, however, calibration at high pressures is not usually necessary.

For measuring total pressure it is possible to use a differential pressure transducer with one side open to the atmosphere, provided that the total pressure is low enough to be within the differential-pressure capacity of the transducer. For high total pressures it is necessary to use a total-pressure transducer, which is designed to bear pressure on one side of the diaphragm only.

A great variety of differential pressure transducers is on the market. When purchasing a transducer for industrial use it is desirable to specify: (a) differential pressure range to be covered; (b) maximum line pressure; (c) maximum and minimum temperature; (d) nature of fluid; and (e) accuracy and/or repeatability required.

If the transducer is intended for laboratory use it may also be necessary to specify response time. Note that short response time and high accuracy do not usually go together. Bear in mind also that if you need fast response it is essential to connect the transducer to the pressure tappings with two equal, very short, lengths of large-bore tubing, and that the wires between the transducer and its 'black box' should also be kept short.

12.1.5 Bellows-type Differential Pressure Gauges

The bellows gauge is a mechanical device developed expressly for the industrial measurement of small differential pressures at high line pressures. It is employed widely in the orifice plate installations used to meter compressed natural gas.

Two bellows filled with liquid are placed end to end in two chambers of a pressure vessel, and their interiors are interconnected through a pipe. Each bellows is exposed to one of the two pressures, and as the differential increases the bellows on the high-pressure side contracts while the other bellows expands. The movement of the bellows is constrained by a system of springs and taken out of the pressure vessel via a linkage and a torque tube, which can operate either a mechanical or a pneumatic readout device.

The advantage of this type of bellows gauge is that it is more compact and convenient than any other accurate mechanical device for measuring differential pressures, whilst, being non-electrical, it is especially suited for use in areas of high fire risk. Versions with an electrical readout are also available.

12.1.6 Free-piston Pressure Gauges

The original form of free-piston gauge is familiar to most engineers as a device for calibrating pressure gauges; in this form it is often termed a deadweight tester. It consists of a small vertical piston fitted into the upper end of a cylinder filled with oil under pressure. There are no seals—the piston is a good sliding fit in the cylinder and the amount of leakage is small enough to be acceptable, whilst stiction is prevented by rotating the piston. Weights on the top of the piston provide a force, and when this is divided by the effective area of the piston the result is an absolute measure of the pressure in the cylinder. For accurate work the local value of the acceleration of gravity must be used in the calculations.

Several important developments from this basic device have brought a variety of other types of free-piston gauge on the market in recent years. Several of these are built for the accurate direct measurement of differential pressure; they either involve two deadweight gauges suitably linked together, or one loaded free-piston capable of being subjected to different pressures at either end. These are all complicated systems requiring highly skilled operators and are therefore best suited for use as primary standards in major standards laboratories.

Another development of wider application is the free-piston pressure balance. It employs some kind of weighing device to measure the force on the piston instead of deadweights, and this renders it much more convenient to operate but not quite so accurate as the deadweight devices. Both total-pressure and differential-pressure forms of free-piston balance are available; they are supplied in versions to cover various ranges from kilobars to millibars, and can be used with both liquids and gases. They are used both as secondary standards for the calibration of working gauges, and as laboratory tools for the direct measurement of total pressure and differential pressure in applications where the highest possible accuracy is needed.

12.2 Temperature Measurement

12.2.1 Thermometer Pockets

A simple way to make an accurate measurement of the temperature of a fluid inside a tank or pipe is with a thermometer pocket, or 'thermowell'. This is simply a metal tube projecting downwards into the pipe or vessel, with its inner end closed and its outer end open, as was shown incidentally in *Figure 11.1b*. The pocket is filled with liquid to facilitate heat transfer, and a mercury-in-glass thermometer—or some other device for measuring temperature—is then inserted into it.

The most important thing to remember about thermometer pockets is that they conduct heat away from the point where the temperature is to be measured and disperse it to the atmosphere. Errors arising from this effect are more or less inversely proportional to the length of the pocket, and proportional to the temperature difference between the fluid and the atmosphere.

It is therefore important that thermometer pockets should not be too short: 100 mm can be regarded as a reasonable minimum length for most situations, but 200 mm is better if high accuracy is required. If the temperature difference between the fluid and the atmosphere is more than a few tens of degrees (or a few degrees in situations where high accuracy is essential, such as calibration tanks) a large area of surface around the mouth of the thermometer pocket should be thermally insulated to reduce thermal losses from the pocket. Formulae are given in books on thermometry from which corrections for heat loss in thermometer pockets can be calculated, but the results given by them are only approximations. Where the temperature difference is very high it is advisable not to use thermometer pockets at all, unless only moderate accuracy is required.

12.2.2 Thermocouples

The thermocouple is widely used for measuring temperature in industrial installations. It is reasonably cheap, it is compact and easy to install, and the output is in the convenient form of a voltage which is practically linear with temperature over a fairly wide range. An accuracy in the region of $\pm 0.5°C$ can be maintained over fairly long periods, and for many purposes this is adequate.

Such disadvantages as it possesses are not very serious. A reference junction has to be provided and maintained at an accurately known temperature, but with modern methods of temperature control this can be done inexpensively, and one enclosure for reference junctions can serve a number of adjacent thermocouples. It conducts some heat away from the sensing area, but to nothing like the same extent as a thermometer pocket because the wires have such a small cross-section; and if conduction ever does become a problem it can usually be cured by running the leads along an isotherm for the first few centimetres back from the sensing junction.

Thermocouples are usually enclosed, either partially or wholly, in some kind of protective shield. This can change their measuring characteristics, and it is therefore important to follow the instructions provided by the supplier or laid down in one of the standard codes for temperature measurement.

12.2.3 Resistance Thermometers

In many areas related to flow measurement the resistance thermometer may prove even more suitable than a thermocouple. Where high accuracy is needed the platinum resistance thermometer is ideal, since the potential accuracy of this device is almost unbelievably high: in the monastic atmosphere of a national standards laboratory accuracies better than a millidegree are commonplace. In the workaday world accuracies of $\pm0.1^{\circ}C$ are easily obtained, and it is not too difficult to improve upon this figure if circumstances should require this.

Temperature measurement systems based on platinum resistance thermometers tend to be expensive. The actual probes are very much more than a piece of platinum wire on the end of a handle; their construction is fairly complicated and they are rather costly devices, as well as being quite easy to break—an unfortunate combination.

Nickel resistance thermometers and semiconductor resistance thermometers, generally known as thermistors, are also widely used. Although less accurate than the platinum type they are cheaper and rather easier to handle. Thermistors are much more sensitive to temperature changes than metal resistance thermometers, but they have a more limited temperature range and they need individual calibration.

12.2.4 Temperature Measurement in Flowing Gases

When a temperature probe is inserted into a stream of flowing gas, it slows the gas down in the vicinity of the probe. This causes both the pressure and the temperature to increase locally, and consequently the probe will over-read.

The effect is proportional to the square of the velocity, and consequently if the gas velocity is only a few metres per second the excess temperature indicated by the probe will be negligible. At a few tens of metres per second the excess may possibly be worth taking into account where high accuracy is called for, and at velocities running into hundreds of metres per second a correction for dynamic heating of the probe will generally be essential.

The dynamic correction for a particular temperature probe may be measured experimentally or it may be estimated from theoretical considerations. But measurement of the correction is tedious, whilst a theoretical calculation will inevitably depend upon a number of assumptions about the probe, and so the result will not be more than an approximation. A simpler solution frequently used in probes designed to measure temperature in fast flowing gases is to design them so that the velocity of the gas across the sensor is reduced and the various errors involved practically cancel out; such probes are termed 'direct reading', since they give acceptable results over a wide range of velocity without the need for any corrections to be applied.

12.3 Density Measurement

The density of a flowing fluid may be determined either by a manual measurement on a sample, or automatically by an on-line densitometer.

12.3.1 Manual Methods for Laboratory Use

There are three main laboratory methods of measuring fluid density of interest to the flowmeter user, which are briefly described below.

(a) *Hydrometers*. These instruments, which are used only with liquids, consist of a float with a long, narrow neck upon which a scale is engraved. The denser the liquid the more the hydrometer neck will project, and the density is indicated by the graduation nearest to the liquid surface. For highly volatile liquids, and some compressed liquid gases such as propane and butane, there are special hydrometers designed for use inside a pressure vessel. Hydrometers are extremely convenient and accuracies between ±1 and ±0.1% can be obtained, depending upon circumstances and the type of hydrometer used.

(b) *Pyknometers*. These are vessels of known weight and volume which can be filled completely with fluid and then weighed, so that the fluid density can then be calculated from its mass and its known volume. They take many forms, some designed for use with gases and others with liquids. One form, which will be familiar to many readers under its old name of 'density bottle', or the even older and now obsolete name of 'specific gravity bottle', is officially known in the petroleum industry as a 'capillary-stoppered pyknometer'. An accuracy of about ±0.1% is obtainable with liquids under industrial laboratory conditions.

(c) *Buoyant Weighing Method*. This is the method which, according to legend, Archimedes invented on the day he ran around in the altogether, crying 'Eureka'. The density of the fluid is inferred from the apparent loss of weight of a body of known volume immersed in it. Although it was originally used only with liquids in open vessels, modern instrumentation has enabled it to be adapted for use inside pressure vessels with both compressed liquids and gases. In its most refined forms it is not an easy method to use but it is extremely accurate, and is generally regarded as the ultimate standard method against which all other instruments for measuring density should be calibrated.

12.3.2 Automatic On-line Methods

The most important instrument for on-line measurement is the vibration density meter, often referred to as a densitometer or densimeter. Fluid is passed through a test cell containing a vibrating element which is usually either a kind of tuning fork or a cylinder with very thin walls. This is excited electromagnetically and a resonant electromagnetic circuit is used to measure the natural frequency of the vibrator, which is a known function of the surrounding fluid. Accuracies of about ±0.02% in liquid and ±0.1% in gas are typical in industrial practice, although the special instruments used in standards laboratories will do better than this.

Several other types of on-line densitometer are still in use, although most of them are now declining in popularity. These include centrifugal devices (used with gas); buoyant weighing instruments (for gases and liquids); gamma radiation densitometers; and an apparatus in which a loop of pipe is coupled to the system through flexible bellows and supported on a load-cell weighing instrument. The last two of these are especially suitable for 'difficult' liquids, which are liable to clog vibrating densitometers.

12.4 Data-processing Devices and Systems

Simple mechanical data-processing devices have been used in association with flowmeters since long before the dawn of the electronics age. The best known of these is perhaps the chart recorder, which produces a graph of flowrate versus time; from this the output of a flowrate meter can be integrated by measuring the area under the graph with a planimeter, thus giving the total volume passed.

Another simple mechanical device is the automatic temperature compensator which is frequently fitted to positive displacement meters used for the measurement of liquid petroleum products. This senses the temperature of the flowing liquid and applies a correction through the gearing in the meter's mechanical register. In consequence the meter indicates the volume of liquid that *would* have passed through *if* the temperature had remained constant at a predetermined reference value, such as 15°C.

Similar, but more complicated, mechanical devices are used to correct the readings of gas meters to standard conditions. These correct for variations in both temperature and pressure, and the more elaborate kinds are even capable of taking non-ideal behaviour of the gas into account.

In large metering installations electronic data-processing devices, including dedicated minicomputers and microprocessors, are now taking over these functions and performing a host of others. More and more meter manufacturers are offering modules that will integrate the output of flowrate meters, feed in the value of calibration factor appropriate to the flowrate, apply corrections for variations in pressure, temperature, viscosity and calorific value, sound an alarm when something goes wrong with the meters, control samplers, invoice customers ... the possibilities are almost limitless.

12.5 Where to Learn More

Information on pressure tappings and manometers is given not only in the references already mentioned[1-4] but also in an ISO Standard[5], which deals in addition with methods of connecting pressure tappings to differential pressure instruments.

There are so many books, standards and papers on the measurement of pressure, temperature and density that it is impractical to mention those of general interest. A few, however, have been written with the interests of flowmeter users in mind, or at least are of special relevance in the field of flow measurement. Among these is a substantial survey paper by Daborn[6] on the accurate measurement of differential pressure at high pressures, and one by Preston[7] on the accurate measurement of very low differential pressures in water flow measurement.

The art of measuring temperature in flowing gases has been well described by Moffat[8]. Temperature measurement in liquids being metered is covered in chapter 7 of the API Manual mentioned in section 13.2.2, as well as in an earlier standard issued by the IP[9]. Another part of this API Manual (sub-chapter 5.4) consists of a brief introduction to the whole field of instrumentation and auxiliary equipment used in conjunction with petroleum meters.

Manual methods of measuring density are dealt with in an existing IP standard[10], and the use of on-line densitometers in oil measurement is the subject of a new IP standard due for publication in 1979. It is also intended that a section on densitometers will be included in the forthcoming revision of the British Standard on differential pressure meters, which was mentioned in Chapter 3. Several ISO standards on various methods of density measurement are due for publication shortly, and one on hydrometers has already been published[11].

References

1   Rayle, R. E., 'Influence of orifice geometry on static pressure measurements', *ASME Paper 59-A-234*, A.S.M.E., New York (1959)
2   Shaw, R., 'The influence of hole dimensions on static pressure measurements', *J. Fluid Mech.*, 7 No. 4, 550–564 (1960)
3   Blake, K. A., 'The design of piezometer rings', *J. Fluid Mech.*, 78 No. 2, 415–428 (1976)

4   *ISA Standard RP 2.1., Manometer tables,* Instrument Society of America, Pittsburgh (1962)
5   *ISO Standard 2186 (1973).* Fluid flow in closed conduits—connections for pressure signal transmissions between primary and secondary elements
6   Daborn, J. E., 'The accurate measurement of differential pressure at high line pressure', *Measurement and Control,* **10** No. 10, 377-387 (1977)
7   Preston, J. H., 'The measurement of pressure in low velocity water flows', *J. Phys. E.,* **5,** 277-282 (1972)
8   Moffat, R. J., 'Gas temperature measurement'. In C. M. Herzfeld (Ed.), *Temperature, its measurement and control in science and industry, Vol. 3, Part 2* (A. I. Dahl (Ed.)), Reinhold, New York (1962). Also Chapman and Hall, London
9   *IP 204/68, Petroleum Measurement Manual, Part IV: Temperature measurement,* Institute of Petroleum, London (1968)
10   *IP 207/71, Petroleum Measurement Manual, Part 7: Relative density and density measurement,* Institute of Petroleum, London (1971)
11   *ISO Standard 3675 (1976).* Petroleum and liquid petroleum products— Determination of density and relative density—Hydrometer method

13

Where to go for Help and Information

Give us the job and we will finish the tools!
An unknown parodist of Churchill

The purpose of this chapter is to bring together a collection of miscellaneous information likely to benefit the flowmeter user faced with the need for calibrations, for advice or for information. Sources of published information on specific areas have already been given in the 'Where to learn more' sections at the end of the earlier chapters; this chapter fills in the gaps by listing the information sources of a more general character.

13.1 Independent Flow Measurement Laboratories and Consultants

Practically every flowmeter manufacturer has his own calibration facilities and some of them are willing to undertake, as a service to clients, the calibration of meters not made by themselves. However, since they are in business to sell their own products they can hardly be expected to offer impartial advice, and flowmeter users generally prefer to have their meters calibrated by a flowmeter testing laboratory which is independent of manufacturers' interests. There are many of these scattered about the world, and they vary enormously in the services they can provide and the fees they charge; it therefore often pays to shop around when you want a meter calibrated.

In most industrialised countries small- or medium-sized liquid quantity meters can often be calibrated at a reasonable cost at a regional or national laboratory of the official Weights and Measures Service. Sometimes the Weights and Measures Department is equipped to calibrate liquid flowrate meters and gas quantity meters of moderate sizes also. Quite a number of universities are also able to provide a reasonably priced calibration service for both quantity and flowrate meters in the smaller sizes.

Where these sources are unable to help—and especially when large flowrates are involved—it is usually necessary to involve one of the larger independent flow measurement laboratories. These not only provide calibration services, but many of them also offer a consultancy service and some provide facilities for carrying out sponsored research and development as well.

A list of the principal government laboratories in various countries is given below. It is followed by a shorter list of private organisations in the same field; this, unfortunately, is less complete, since information about such bodies in other countries is hard to obtain.

More detailed information about some of the calibration centres mentioned is given in a publication[1] issued by the NEL, in collaboration with the ISO.

13.1.1 Major Government Laboratories

United Kingdom

The main British centre for flowmeter research is the Flow Measurement Division of the National Engineering Laboratory at East Kilbride, Glasgow. This boasts the most comprehensive collection of flow measurement facilities in the world, with about a dozen systems for calibrating both quantity and flowrate meters with water, oil, fuel, air and compressed air. NEL also offers a full service of consultancy, on-site testing and laboratory investigations. Other public-sector laboratories in Britain with more limited interests include the Central Electricity Generating Board's Hydraulic Calibration Centre at Hams Hall, Sutton Coldfield (water); the Department of Energy's Gas Standards Laboratory at Leicester; the Hydraulic Research Station at Wallingford (current meters); the UKAEA's Radioisotopes in Industry Unit, Harwell (tracer methods); and the National Maritime Institute at Teddington (anemometers and current meters).

United States

There is less government involvement in industrial research in the USA than in Europe, and the only major establishment in the field owned by the US Government appears to be the National Bureau of Standards. Its main laboratories at Gaithersburg, near Washington D.C., have responsibilities for the Weights and Measures aspects of metering and for general research into flowmeters, whilst its outstation at Boulder, Colorado, has the western world's only independent facility for the accurate calibration of cryogenic meters on liquid nitrogen.

Japan

The main Japanese government-owned research centre concerned with flowmeters is the National Research Laboratory for Metrology at Kaga, Itabashi-Ku, Tokyo.

France

The field here is divided between the Water Meter Laboratory in the Avenue
P.V. Couturier, Paris, and the research centre of Gaz de France at Alfortville.

Germany

Flowmeter work in Germany is centred on the PTB Laboratories at Brunswick,
which have responsibilities both for Weights and Measures and for industrial
services.

Italy

The Italian centre is the Institute of Metrology in the Strada Delle Cacce, Turin.

Netherlands

Water meters are the province of the Waterloopkundig Laboratorium at Delft,
and gas meters of Nederlandse Gasunie at Groningen.

USSR

Of the various Soviet laboratories concerned with flowmeter calibration, the
one best known in the West is the Kazan Institute, which can be contacted
through the State Committee of Standards, Leninsky Prospekt 96, Moscow.

13.1.2 Privately-owned Calibration Centres

United Kingdom

The SIRA Institute at Chislehurst is an independent research centre serving
the whole scientific instrument industry. It has facilities for calibrating flowmeters with oil and water, and specialises in life-testing and performance evaluation of flowmeters. Two companies based in London operate portable pipe
provers and volumetric tanks, with which they and their foreign affiliates
provide on-site calibration services for the petroleum and process industries in
Britain and overseas: they are Caleb Brett and Son Ltd., and the company with
which the author is associated, Redwood International Consultants Ltd. These
companies also provide a flowmeter consultancy service.

United States

Facilities for calibrating meters with water at extremely high flowrates are
available at the St. Anthony Falls Hydraulic Laboratory, which belongs to the
University of Minnesota, Minneapolis. Other water facilities with a rather lower

(but still very high) maximum flowrate capacity are provided by the Alden Research Laboratories of the Worcester Polytechnic Institute, Massachusetts. High-pressure gas meters can be calibrated at the Colorado Engineering Experimental Station, Nunn, Colorado. On-site calibration of oil and fuel meters is carried out by such companies as Metric Inc. of Tulsa, and Southern Petroleum Laboratories of Lafayette.

France

At the TRAPIL Meter Testing Station, Gennevilliers, oil meters of all sizes can be calibrated accurately against static pipe provers with a variety of test liquids.

13.2 Standardising Bodies and their Standards

In the earlier chapters a considerable number of national and international standard specifications have been cited. These represent only the tip of a very cumbersome iceberg, since many bodies are involved in drawing up standards affecting flowmeters, and their combined output is quite considerable. For a more detailed account of the international scene reference can be made to a paper by Irwin[2] and a BSI publication[3], but the outline given below will probably be sufficient for most readers.

13.2.1 Official National Bodies

Every industrialised nation has its own national standards organisation, which is always officially recognised and usually backed in some positive way by the government, but is not normally a part of the civil service. Such bodies are almost invariably known by a collection of initials or an acronym—BSI (British), ANSI (American), AFNOR (French) and DIN (German) being the best known in the English-speaking world. They produce standard specifications for the guidance and assistance of manufacturers and users of equipment.

In addition every major country has its national Weights and Measures Service, the headquarters of which is generally a national government department, although the field services may often be under local government control, as they are in Britain. These bodies make regulations which are enforced by law to govern the selling of commodities by weight, length, area and volume, so as to protect customers from being defrauded. When they affect the metering of fluids for purposes of trade, these regulations are, in effect, flow measurement standards with a limited field of use.

Finally, there are usually one or two government departments concerned with raising revenue on the production, import or sales of liquids and gases. In Britain these are H.M. Customs and Excise who levy duties on excisable liquids, and the Department of Energy who collect royalties on oil and gas produced in British

territory. For their own purposes they also draw up regulations which act more
or less as standards for certain metering operations with which they are concerned.

Within any one country there has to be a close liaison between the various
official bodies mentioned above and the industry-oriented ones mentioned below,
to ensure that their various standards and regulations are not in serious conflict.

13.2.2 Industry-oriented National Bodies

In Britain, practically all the standard specifications and codes of practice—but
not, of course, government regulations—for the metering of petroleum and its
products are drawn up by the Institute of Petroleum's numerous standardisation
committees. The IP is officially regarded as a learned society, although it is
concerned with industrial matters to a considerable extent. Its standards are
held in high esteem by the petroleum industry throughout the world, but they
have no official status; this means that they cannot be recognised as British
standards unless and until the BSI formally adopts them. In practice the links
between BSI and IP are very strong, and are essential in the modern world
because of the international implications—a number of IP standards have, in
fact, been used as the basis of international standards (see section 13.2.3 below).

The Institute has issued a group of standards which are known collectively as
the IP Petroleum Measurement Manual, but most of these are concerned with
what is known in the industry as 'static measurement', which means determination of total volume by using dipsticks or tank gauges. The various parts of the
Manual are published as separate booklets, and those few which are relevant to
metering have been mentioned earlier in this book. Several proposed new IP
codes—which will not necessarily be issued as parts of the Manual—are directly
concerned with metering and meter calibration, however; they are due to be
issued over the next few years.

The American Petroleum Institute is more of an industrial association and less
like a learned society than the IP. The API's standardising activities form only a
minor part of its total interests, but even so its output of standards concerned
with oil metering is currently much greater than that of the IP. Many of these
standards are already used throughout the world, and form the basis of existing
or proposed ISO standards (see section 13.2.3). The various chapters and sub-
chapters of the API's new 'Manual of Petroleum Measurement Standards' are
beginning to appear in print at the time of writing, and by the time this book
is published the Manual should be nearly complete.

The chapters or proposed chapters of most interest to the meter user are:
chapter 4, which has six separate sub-chapters dealing with meter calibration
(or 'meter proving', as it is known in the oil industry); chapter 5, which has
four separate sub-chapters on meters and metering; chapter 6, which is concerned
with metering under special conditions; chapter 7, on temperature measurement;
chapter 11, which contains *PVT* data for hydrocarbons, water and certain solids,
in forms that facilitate metering computations; sub-chapter 12.2, which sets out

procedures for metering calculations; chapter 13, which offers guidance on the use of statistical methods for estimating the accuracy of measurement; and sub-chapter 14.3, which deals with orifice plates for metering natural gas. Some of these chapters are being prepared and issued in collaboration with the IP.

Other bodies issuing standards of interest to flowmeter users include the Institution of Gas Engineers (IGE), the Instrument Society of America (ISA), the American Gas Association (AGA), the American Society for Testing and Materials (ASTM) and the American Society of Mechanical Engineers (ASME). Some of their standards relating directly to flow measurement have already been mentioned in earlier chapters. The comprehensive ISA book of Standards[4] contains much to interest the flowmeter user, including abstracts of numerous standards issued by various other organisations.

13.2.3 Official International Bodies

At present there are three fully international organisations and one European organisation issuing standards relating to the use of flowmeters.

International Organisation of Legal Metrology (OIML)

The OIML, which is based in the Rue Turgot, Paris, has as its constituent members the Weights and Measures Department of more than 40 of the world's national governments. It has already issued several standards concerned with the Weights and Measures aspects of metering (officially termed 'Recommendations') which have been mentioned in earlier chapters, and others are pending. The steering committees dealing with these are known as Pilot Secretariats 5 and 6, which are concerned with liquid meters and gas meters, respectively. They harmonise the outputs of the individual working groups specialising in various aspects of metering.

International Standards Organisation (ISO)

This body, which has its headquarters in the Rue de Varembe, Geneva, produces most of the international standards concerned with the use of flowmeters outside the context of Weights and Measures. Although the ISO is independent of the OIML a close liaison is maintained between the two organisations. The ISO member bodies are the *official* national standards institutions—such as BSI and ANSI—of more than 80 countries. Unofficial bodies cannot belong to ISO; this means that, in theory, organisations such as the IP and the API are supposed to do all their international standards work by using their national standards institutions as intermediaries. In practice the direct links between such bodies and the ISO are often quite strong. A considerable number of ISO standards have been mentioned in earlier chapters, and a good many more are likely to be published over the next few years. The ISO Technical Committees involved in this work are TC 30–Measurement of Fluid Flow in Closed Conduits; TC 113–Measurement of Liquid Flow in Open Channels; TC 28/SC 2–Dynamic Petroleum Measurement; and TC 28/SC 5–Natural Gas Fluids Measurement.

International Electrotechnical Commission (IEC)

It is a sad reflection on the human race's reluctance to agree and to standardise that the IEC should exist separately from the ISO. It is the same kind of organisation, with much the same national institutions eligible for membership, and it even has the same address in Geneva as ISO, with which it is formally affiliated. There are, however, some important differences in operating procedure. The line of demarcation between their respective areas–IEC deals with electrical and ISO with non-electrical standards–is fuzzy and sometimes movable, because in practice it is impossible to draw a precise boundary. So it happens, for example, that liquid turbine meters, which have an electrical readout, are nevertheless in the province of ISO, whilst IEC, through its committee SC 65B, has now taken over from ISO the responsibility for pneumatically operated flow control valves. In general, ISO now issues standards for flowmeters whilst IEC is concerned with secondary instruments such as differential pressure transducers, for which an IEC standard is contemplated.

European Economic Community (EEC)

The Council of the EEC is issuing a series of standards, officially termed 'directives', on the metering of fluids. These are intended for use in the field of Weights and Measures, and they generally conform with the spirit–though not necessarily the wording–of the parallel OIML standards. The most important EEC directives issued so far have been mentioned in the relevant chapters of this book.

13.3 Other Sources of Information

13.3.1 General Textbooks on Flow Measurement

A number of books dealing with limited areas of the field of flow measurement have already been mentioned in Chapters 3, 6, 7 and 8. There are also a few books covering a wider range of flowmeters, of which the most important are probably Ower and Pankhurst[5], Spink[6] and the ASME book, Fluid Meters[7]. The first of these is British in origin and the others American; they are all in print at the time of writing. Two earlier British books[8,9] are still useful even though they are now out of print, since they are available in numerous libraries.

   None of these books covers nearly as large an area as this book, but what they do cover they generally deal with in greater depth.

13.3.2 Abstracts and Bibliographies

For keeping abreast of developments in the whole field of flow measurement, there is a bi-monthly abstract journal[10], which is prepared jointly by the British Hydromechanics Research Association and the National Engineering Laboratory. This began publication in 1974.

For references to earlier work there are three substantial bibliographies. The BHRA's so-called bibliography (it is really a collection of abstracts) on fluid flow measurement[11] covers mainly the two decades before the above-mentioned abstracts journal began publication. Redding's collection of abstracts on orifice plates and nozzles[12] was published in 1952.

The monumental bibliography on hydrometry[13] published by Kolupaila in 1961 is biassed towards open channel flow measurement, but still contains numerous useful references to early publications on flowmeters in several languages. Many of the references are unaccompanied by abstracts, but where abstracts are given they are usually helpful and sometimes delightfully colourful, with openings such as, 'Splendid publication of . . .', and, 'A very interesting and valuable report . . .'.

13.3.3 Conferences and Conference Proceedings

Major international conferences devoted solely to flow measurement have been held every year or two of late, and the published proceedings of these conferences[14-18] are a mine of information on recent developments. One of these[14] is the largest collection of writings on flow measurement ever made, with 163 papers occupying three volumes of some 500 pages each.

Also, the triennial international 'Imeko' conferences, although concerned with the whole field of scientific and industrial measurement, usually have a good sprinkling of high-quality papers on flowmeters: the published proceedings[19] of the latest in the series, Imeko VII which was held in London in 1976, contain about a dozen.

13.3.4 Lecture Courses

A number of instruction courses on various aspects of flow metering are held from time to time in the United States. The oldest and most famous of these is the International School of Hydrocarbon Measurement, which is held every year at the University of Oklahoma. It is concerned with the metering of natural gas and petroleum liquids.

Similar courses do not appear to have been held in Britain until 1977, when the National Engineering Laboratory offered a general course on the principles and practice of flow measurement, and Redwood International Consultants Ltd. offered one on the metering of petroleum liquids. Both courses were so successful that they have already had to be repeated several times. So it rather looks as if regular courses on the use of flowmeters will soon have become a feature of the engineering scene in Britain, just as they already are in America.

13.3.5 'Where-to-Buy' Information

The association known as SIRAID (phone 01-467-5555 between 1000 and 1200 or 1400 and 1600 hours) is able to list sources of supply for almost all types of measuring instrument.

References

1   Scott, R. W. W., *NEL Report No. 622, Flow measurement calibration facilities of the world*, National Engineering Laboratory, East Kilbride, Glasgow (1976)

2   Irwin, L. K., 'An anatomy of the international standards producing system—flow measurement', in Reference 17 below, 895–920

3   *Short guide to international organisations concerned with standards*, British Standards Institution, London (1977)

4   *Standards and practices for instrumentation*, 5th edn., Instrument Society of America, Pittsburgh (1977)

5   Ower, E. and Pankhurst, R. C., *The measurement of air flow*, 5th edn., Pergamon, Oxford and New York (1977)

6   Spink, L. K., *Principles and practice of flowmeter engineering*, 9th edn., The Foxboro Co., Foxboro, Mass. (1967)

7   Bean, H. S. (Ed.), *Fluid Meters*, 6th edn., American Society of Mechanical Engineers, New York (1971)

8   Linford, A., *Flow measurement and meters*, 2nd edn., Spon, London (1961)

9   Preston, T. D. (Ed.), *Shell flowmeter engineering handbook*, Bataafse Internationale Petroleum Maatschappij N.V., The Hague (1968)

10 *Fluid flow measurement abstracts*, published bi-monthly since January 1974 by BHRA Fluid Engineering, Cranfield, Bedford

11 Dowden, R. R., *Fluid flow measurement: a bibliography*, BHRA Fluid Engineering, Cranfield, Bedford (1972)

12 Redding, T. H., *A bibliography survey of flow through orifices and parallel-throated nozzles*, Chapman and Hall, London (1952)

13 Kolupaila, S., *Bibliography of hydrometry*, University of Notre Dame Press, Notre Dame, Indiana (1961)

14 Clayton, C. G. (Ed.), *Modern developments in flow measurement* (Proc. Int. Conf. at Harwell, Berks., Sept. 1971), Peregrinus, London (1972)

15 Dowell, R. B. (Ed.), *Flow, its measurement and control in science and industry* (Proc. Int. Conf. at Pittsburgh, Pa., May 1971), Instrument Society of America, Pittsburgh (1974)

16 Spencer, E. A. and Ramsay, W. J. (Eds.), *Fluid flow measurement in the mid-1970s* (Proc. Int. Conf. at East Kilbride, Glasgow, April 1975), HMSO, Edinburgh (1977)

17 Irwin, L. K. (Ed.), *Flow measurement in open channels and closed conduits* (Proc. Int. Conf. at Gaithersburg, Maryland, February 1977), US Department of Commerce, Washington, D.C. (1977)

18 Dijstelbergen, H. H. and Spencer, E. A. (Eds.), *Flow measurement of fluids:*
    Flomeko, 1978 (Proc. Int. Conf. at Groningen, Netherlands, September 1978),
    North-Holland, Amsterdam (in the press)
19 Striker, Gy. (Ed.), *Practical measurement for improving efficiency—Acta*
    Imeko 1976 (Proc. 7th Int. Congress of Int. Measurement Confederation,
    May 1976), North-Holland, Amsterdam (1977)

Appendix: SI Conversion Tables for Quantities Used in Flow Measurement

Area
$1 \text{ m}^2 = 1.076\ 39 \times 10 \text{ ft}^2$
$1 \text{ m}^2 = 1.550\ 00 \times 10^3 \text{ in}^2$
$1 \text{ mm}^2 = 1.550\ 00 \times 10^{-3} \text{ in}^2$

$1 \text{ ft}^2 = 9.290\ 30 \times 10^{-2} \text{ m}^2$
$1 \text{ in}^2 = 6.451\ 60 \times 10^{-4} \text{ m}^2$
$1 \text{ in}^2 = 6.451\ 60 \times 10^2 \text{ mm}^2$

Density
$1 \text{ kg m}^3 = 1 \text{ g l}^{-1} = 6.242\ 79 \times 10^{-2} \text{ lb ft}^{-3}$
$1 \text{ kg l}^{-1} = 1.002\ 24 \times 10 \text{ lb (Imp. gal)}^{-1}$
$1 \text{ kg l}^{-1} = 8.345\ 40 \text{ lb (US gal)}^{-1}$

$1 \text{ lb ft}^{-3} = 1.601\ 85 \times 10 \text{ kg m}^{-3} \text{ (g l}^{-1})$
$1 \text{ lb (Imp. gal)}^{-1} = 9.977\ 64 \times 10^{-2} \text{ kg l}^{-1}$
$1 \text{ lb (US gal)}^{-1} = 1.198\ 26 \times 10^{-1} \text{ kg l}^{-1}$

Flowrate (Volumetric)
$1 \text{ l s}^{-1} = 2.118\ 88 \text{ ft}^3 \text{ min}^{-1}$
$1 \text{ l s}^{-1} = 1.319\ 81 \times 10 \text{ Imp. gal min}^{-1}$
$1 \text{ l s}^{-1} = 1.585\ 03 \times 10 \text{ US gal min}^{-1}$

$1 \text{ ft}^3 \text{ min}^{-1} = 4.719\ 47 \times 10^{-1} \text{ l s}^{-1}$
$1 \text{ Imp. gal min}^{-1} = 7.576\ 84 \times 10^{-2} \text{ l s}^{-1}$
$1 \text{ US gal min}^{-1} = 6.309\ 03 \times 10^{-2} \text{ l s}^{-1}$

Flowrate (Mass)
$1 \text{ kg s}^{-1} = 1.322\ 77 \text{ lb min}^{-1}$
$1 \text{ kg s}^{-1} = 7.936\ 64 \times 10^3 \text{ lb h}^{-1}$
$1 \text{ kg s}^{-1} = 3.543\ 13 \text{ ton h}^{-1}$

$1 \text{ lb min}^{-1} = 7.559\ 87 \times 10^{-3} \text{ kg s}^{-1}$
$1 \text{ lb h}^{-1} = 1.259\ 98 \times 10^{-4} \text{ kg s}^{-1}$
$1 \text{ ton h}^{-1} = 2.822\ 35 \times 10^{-1} \text{ kg s}^{-1}$

Length
$1 \text{ m} = 3.280\ 84 \text{ ft}$
$1 \text{ m} = 3.937\ 01 \text{ in}$

$1 \text{ ft} = 3.048\ 00 \times 10^{-1} \text{ m}$
$1 \text{ in} = 2.540\ 00 \times 10^{-2} \text{ m}$

contd. overleaf

Mass (note: 1 tonne = 10^3 kg)

1 kg = 2.204 62 lb

1 kg = 9.842 05 $\times 10^{-4}$ ton

1 lb = 4.535 92 $\times 10^{-1}$ kg

1 ton = 1.016 05 $\times 10^{-3}$ kg

Pressure (note: 1 bar = 10^5 Pa)

1 bar = 1.450 38 $\times 10$ lbf in^{-2}

1 bar = 4.014 63 $\times 10^2$ inH$_2$O

1 bar = 2.953 00 $\times 10$ inHg

1 bar = 1.019 72 kgf cm^{-2}

1 lbf in^{-2} = 6.894 76 $\times 10^{-2}$ bar

1 inH$_2$O = 2.490 89 $\times 10^{-3}$ bar

1 inHg = 3.386 39 $\times 10^{-2}$ bar

1 kgf cm^{-2} = 9.806 65 $\times 10^{-1}$ bar

Specific Volume

1 m^3 kg^{-1} = 1.601 85 $\times 10$ ft^3 lb^{-1}

1 l kg^{-1} = 9.977 64 $\times 10^{-2}$ Imp. gal lb^{-1}

1 l kg^{-1} = 1.198 26 $\times 10^{-1}$ US gal lb^{-1}

1 ft^3 lb^{-1} = 6.242 79 $\times 10^{-2}$ m^3 kg^{-1}

1 Imp. gal lb^{-1} = 1.002 24 $\times 10$ l kg^{-1}

1 US gal lb^{-1} = 8.345 40 l kg^{-1}

Velocity

1 m s^{-1} = 3.280 84 ft s^{-1}

1 m s^{-1} = 1.968 50 $\times 10^2$ ft min^{-1}

1 ft s^{-1} = 3.048 00 $\times 10^{-1}$ m s^{-1}

1 ft min^{-1} = 5.080 00 $\times 10^{-3}$ m s^{-1}

Viscosity (absolute) (note: 1 cP = 1 mPa s = 10^{-3} N s m^{-2})

1 cP = 6.719 71 $\times 10^{-4}$ lb ft^{-1} s^{-1}

1 lb ft^{-1} s^{-1} = 1.488 16 $\times 10^3$ cP

Viscosity (kinematic) (note: 1 cSt = 10^{-6} m^2 s^{-1})

1 cSt = 1.076 39 $\times 10^{-5}$ ft^2 s^{-1}

1 ft^2 s^{-1} = 9.290 30 $\times 10^4$ cSt

Volume (note: 1 l = 10^{-3} m^3; 42 US gal = 1 barrel)

1 m^3 = 3.531 47 $\times 10$ ft^3

1 l = 2.199 69 $\times 10^{-1}$ Imp. gal

1 l = 2.641 72 $\times 10^{-1}$ US gal

1 ft^3 = 2.831 68 $\times 10^{-2}$ m^3

1 Imp. gal = 4.546 09 l

1 US gal = 3.785 41 l

Author Index

Subject Index